ST. ANTHONY AND THE CHRIST CHILD

St. Anthony and The Christ Child

by HELEN WALKER HOMAN

illustrated by Don Lynch

VISION BOOKS

Farrar, Straus & Cudahy   New York
Burns & Oates   London

Nihil Obstat:
Rt. Rev. Msgr. Peter B. O'Connor
Censor Librorum

Imprimatur:
✠ Most Reverend Thomas A. Boland, S.T.D.
Archbishop of Newark

To

ANTHONY BELL GREENE

Contents

Author's Note

Author's Note

The story of Saint Anthony and his devotion to the Christ Child, as presented here for young readers, follows the recognized biographies of the universally loved saint in the generally accepted facts, dates, and events.

The personalities whose destinies were intermingled with his have also been recorded in the name and status accorded them by these authorities.

All the historians, however, have confessed to a limitation of known facts concerning the youthful Fernando of Lisbon who became Anthony of Padua. In order to interpret more fully the life of a boy who became one of the greatest saints of Christendom, and a Doctor of the Church, it was necessary to invent certain characters, scenes, and dialogue dealing mainly with his childhood.

It is known that in later life, Anthony, as a Friar Minor, always traveled with a companion who is usually recorded anonymously in the accepted accounts. For simplicity of narration, the author has used the device of creating a single character as a companion in these many and diverse journeys.

Among the sources which were of great assistance was the rich lore of the early Franciscan literature, and, in modern biography, *Enter St. Anthony*, by Father Isidore O'Brien, O.F.M. (St. Anthony Guild Press, 1932) and *A Rich Young Man*, by John E. Beahn (Bruce, 1953).

A word of appreciation is also due to Father Irenaeus, O.F.M., the librarian of the great library of St. Bonaventure University, who generously afforded access to the riches he guards.

St. Anthony and the Christ Child

Chapter One

Glitter of Swords

Sunlight filtered down through a high, narrow slit in the castle wall and struck fire to the gleaming helmets and breastplates which lined the armory. Outside, the hot Portuguese sun of a July day beat down upon the fields, burning them to a crisp. But within the thick stone walls of the Castle de Bulhom, it was cool. The year was 1208.

Fernando stood alone in the long armory. It lay quite far from the great hall where, at that moment, his father and mother were entertaining a company of knights who had ridden over from the capital on the king's business.

Such guests came often to the Castle de Bulhom, for Fernando's father, Don Martinho, was the chief magistrate of the city of Lisbon. The king looked to him to keep order in the busy port and in the rich city which climbed the hills behind it.

During the meal, Fernando had sat close to his father on a dais at the end of the great hall and next to his mother, the beautiful Doña Maria Tereza, of the noble house of Tavera. But when the pages began to carry in more wine and silver bowls overflowing with ripe fruit, he had whispered to her:

"May I be excused, Mother? It's almost time for my lesson with Sir Juan."

Doña Tereza had looked down, smiling, at the eager, thin young face turned to hers, and had nodded. Fernando loved to see his mother smile, for when she did her great dark eyes smiled, too, and gleamed softly like the jewels at her throat. He pressed her hand in thanks and slipped off the bench, glad to escape from the hall and the noisy talk and laughter. Running through the long stone corridors to his favorite haunt, he reached the armory before Sir Juan.

He never tired of handling the shining weapons which hung from its walls. There were swords of all sizes, and spears, and daggers fashioned of the fine steel of Toledo. The great bows and the sharp-pointed arrows took almost a wall to themselves, for in case of an attack, it would be the bowmen who would stand first on the high battlements to repel the enemy.

A company of men-at-arms lived close to the castle's outer wall, and the castle itself housed a dozen knights with their squires. Sir Juan was in command of them all.

Fernando was testing the point of a sword when the knight commander entered. The boy turned quickly at the sound of his step upon the stone floor.

"So, my young friend, you have selected the best sword, as usual! And what have you left for your teacher, eh?"

"Oh, you may take this one," smiled Fernando, holding it up to the giant of a man who was laughing down at him.

They made a strange contrast, these two who stood there in the armory. Fernando was almost thirteen. He had been born on August 15, on the day set aside to honor our Lady, in the year 1195. He was small for his age, and slender; the red silk doublet he wore, and the long hose, hung loosely from his bones. But it was his wide forehead, his attractive, lively face with the large black eyes, and the quick, merry smile at which people looked.

Sir Juan towered above him. With his broad shoulders and his powerful arms, he was as tall and as strong as an oak. He held his head high, as a warrior should, and on his face there was the stamp of

Spain: a high-bridged nose and an underlip that slightly protruded.

Sir Juan came from the Spanish kingdom of Castile, which lay to the east of Portugal. He was every inch a knight, and he served Fernando's father, Don Martinho, with a loyal heart. Together the two had fought many a fierce battle against the Moors. Across Sir Juan's cheek there ran a long scar left there by a Moorish blade when he was fighting in Don Martinho's service.

The knight did not accept the sword which the boy held out to him but turned and chose another from the wall. Now he set about attaching thick corks to the points of each so that they would be well covered.

"On guard, Master Fernando!" cried he, taking his stand in the middle of the armory and flourishing his blade. "And remember well, now, all the things I have taught you!"

Fernando scrambled to his place and crossed his sword with that of the big knight. But almost at every thrust Sir Juan stopped him to show how he had been too fast here, or too slow there, and to make him go through the swordplay again.

"Enough!" cried Sir Juan at last.

As the lad rested, breathless, the knight said:

"You have remembered well what I taught you last time about your feet and throwing your weight. But you have not yet mastered the thrusts. No matter. That will come in time when your wrist is stronger."

The boy looked down at his wrist and wondered how long he would have to wait to see it grow as large and as strong as that of his teacher. It was all very discouraging. Sir Juan saw the troubled look in the big black eyes and said cheerfully, "You are quick on your feet, which is excellent. And you are already a good horseman. Riding will help to strengthen those wrists. And remember that no lad ever became a knight at the age of thirteen!"

Fernando gazed up at the armor on the walls, glimmering in the sunlight. He walked over to a large shield which hung somewhat apart from the others and touched it reverently. It appeared to be very ancient.

"How old was *he* when he became a knight?" he asked.

Sir Juan had followed him and now flung an arm across his shoulder.

"Your ancestor, the great Godfrey de Bouillon? He who freed the Holy Land for Christ and took Jerusalem from the Saracens?"

"Yes," nodded Fernando. "How old was he?"

"Quite young. But you must remember that he was the strongest and bravest knight ever to ride on a crusade. He wasn't yet forty when he took Jerusalem for the Christian armies."

"I wish he had not lived so long ago," sighed Fernando. "I wish I had known him."

"It wasn't so far back, as history goes," said Sir Juan, laying aside his sword and stretching out his great length upon a bench. "It's little more than a hundred years since he took Jerusalem. That was in the First Crusade, in the year 1099."

He folded his arms under his head, and Fernando sat at his feet.

"Tell me about him," urged the boy.

This was how the lessons always ended—with Sir Juan recounting tales of Fernando's ancestor and of many other heroes of the past.

"Godfrey de Bouillon came from the north, from France. His father was the Count of Boulogne. His mother was the daughter of Duke Godfrey of Lorraine. Your ancestor was a powerful warrior and leader of men. Nothing was dearer to him than war —except God. It was God he loved most of all. And he determined that he would give his life to redeeming from the infidels the holy places where God's Son had walked when upon earth. He sold all his possessions to lead the crusade."

"And he won a great battle at the gates of Jerusalem!" chimed in Fernando, his eyes glowing. "And they wanted to make him king, but he refused! Then later, after he died, the Christians lost Jerusalem again. If he had lived, we would have held it!"

"Well," said Sir Juan, "we may win it again. It's never too late to try!"

The knight sat up and grinned happily. "How

would you like that, my young rooster?" he asked, thumping the boy heartily on the back.

"Ouch!" cried Fernando, tenderly feeling his spine.

"Godfrey de Bouillon never said 'ouch!'" reminded his teacher. "What you need, my lad, is more flesh on those skinny bones."

Fernando laughed and said, "You haven't yet told me about my great-grandfather."

"Ah, Don Raoul! *There* was a man for you!" cried Sir Juan, his face lighting up. "The fact that our Lisbon is a Christian city today we owe to him and to the brave crusaders who came from the north in 1147 to throw out the Moors.

"Don Raoul de Bulhom (how the name became changed from de Bouillon to de Bulhom, no one knows) liked Lisbon so much that he settled here with his wife and family," continued Sir Juan.

"Was it he who built this castle?" asked Fernando.

"No, it was his son, Roberto, your own grandfather, who built Castle de Bulhom. He built it strongly and well to repel attacks. And he also built it wisely, high above the city, on St. George's Hill, where its back would be protected by the great stone cliffs."

"And also by the Fortress of St. George which rises above it," reminded Fernando.

"Yes. Your grandfather, Don Roberto de Bulhom, was a wise man."

"How old was my father when Don Roberto let him ride away to become a knight?" asked Fernando.

"Well, your father was about thirteen when he was sent far to the north to become a squire in the service of the king's brother. You know that one has to be a squire first before one can become a knight."

"I am now almost thirteen!" exclaimed Fernando eagerly. "It is time that I, too, were sent away as a squire to some great prince!"

Sir Juan turned his glance from the boy's earnest gaze and walked over to the wall to examine the carved hilt of a Toledo dagger. He did not answer at once.

"Don't you agree, Sir Juan?" pressed Fernando.

The big knight turned slowly and came and sat down beside him again.

"What is it that you want most to be when you grow up?" he asked, his hand on the boy's shoulder.

"A knight, of course, and a crusader!" cried Fernando. "I thought you knew that!"

"Hmm," said Sir Juan.

"Didn't you just say that we might still take Jerusalem?"

"And you want to lead the crusade like your ancestor, Godfrey?" smiled the knight, a twinkle in his eyes. Fernando hung his head.

"I did not say that I wanted to *lead* it," he murmured, "but only to fight in it. And now it's time that I were sent away to be a squire, the more quickly to become a knight!"

Sir Juan looked down at the small figure at his side.

"You are your father's only son. If you were to leave him now, who then would take care of the accounts of Castle de Bulhom?"

"Who cares about the accounts?" cried Fernando, jumping up and gazing fiercely at the knight. "I'm sick of them, anyway!"

"Canon Rodriguez, at the cathedral, says that you are better at numbers than any boy in the school," said Sir Juan gently. "Why don't you continue to study and become a great scholar?"

Fernando was hurt and could not keep back the tears which welled in his eyes.

"I don't want to be a scholar! I want to be a crusader!" he insisted.

"Look, lad," said Sir Juan kindly, "the good God, in His wisdom, has given you a small body. He must have meant you to be that way for something special He wants of you. Unless you grow mightily as the year passes, and unless you put more flesh upon those bones, it is a question whether you can ever be accepted as a squire. It is better that you know this now rather than later."

Fernando's black eyes blazed with anger.

"I will yet grow tall and strong!" he cried. "You will see! And I *will* become a squire and a knight!"

With that he angrily flung himself from the armory. But once his back was turned, he could not see for the tears in his eyes. He had to feel his way through the corridors. No one was about.

At last he found the winding stairway which led up to his mother's apartments. He paused for a moment on the stairs and pressed his hot face against the silent wall. The cool stone comforted him.

Chapter Two

Road Up the Hill

FERNANDO was up early the next morning. The sun was just rising when he dashed down the dark stairs, fastening his doublet as he ran. He tugged at the huge, iron-studded door until it opened a crack to let him slip out and into the wide courtyard beyond.

He sped past the stables where the knights kept their horses, and on to the great gates which led into a covered stone passage, and thence to the road. A sentry greeted him sleepily and opened the gates for him.

"God's morning, Master Fernando!"

"God's morning, Enriquo," cried the boy over his shoulder as he ran on.

Coming out upon the road, he slowed his pace to a walk, not because the road ran up a steep hill, but because he wanted to watch the sun touching the trees and to hear the sleepy birds awaken.

At first, all you could hear was one tiny chirp. Then there would come an answering chirp. Then, almost at once, the air was full of chirps as the birds roused and stretched themselves in their beds, greeting one another and exchanging their plans for the day.

It was going to be a beautiful day, thought Fernando, as he walked up the hill under the archway of green branches. His heart felt light and happy—not at all as it had felt yesterday before he had talked with his mother.

He had found her in her room at the top of the stairs, sitting before a loom and weaving the fine linen which he and his father wore beneath their doublets. The feast in the great hall was over. When she saw him she had known at once that something was wrong. She had pushed aside her work, and he had flung himself at her feet and poured out all his talk with Sir Juan. Doña Tereza listened quietly.

"I am very angry with Sir Juan," finished Fernando, frowning. "I can never forgive him!"

The color rose under his smooth, olive skin. His mother leaned forward and stroked the thick, black hair.

"You must not feel that way, my son. You know that anger is sin, one of the most deadly. And, also, you know in your heart that Sir Juan loves you dearly. Why, you two have been the best of friends almost since the day you were born!"

"But he should not have said that," mumbled Fernando, the tears again welling in his eyes. "He *knows* how much I want to become a knight!"

"Whatever Sir Juan said, he meant only to help you," Doña Tereza answered softly. She was silent for a moment and then said, "Perhaps that was his way of getting you to do all the things that your mother has wanted you to do these past months—things that would make you grow tall and put flesh on your bones."

Fernando hung his head and was silent, remembering how little attention he had paid to his mother's words when they were at table. Doña Tereza was always urging him to eat things he did not like. She was forever pressing food upon him when he wasn't hungry.

Now he felt ashamed as he recalled how often he had deceived her. At table he had waited until her head was turned and she was engaged in lively talk with his father. Then he had quickly emptied half of his plate underneath the table, where, on the stone floor, lay Jingo, his favorite hound. The dog devoured it, and his mother had been none the wiser.

"Look at me, son," now said Doña Tereza.

Fernando lifted his head unhappily and was glad to see that his mother was smiling.

"We will play a joke on Sir Juan," she said with a happy little laugh, her big eyes twinkling. "We will fool him and prove that he is wrong!"

"How?" asked Fernando, eagerly.

"You will be a good son and force yourself to eat. I will see that you get more milk, and beef, and eggs. And every day you must drink milk in midmorning and again in midafternoon."

Fernando screwed up his nose and his mouth in distaste.

"Now don't make a face. You can learn to like milk if you try. Besides, you want to become a knight, don't you?"

"Oh, yes!" cried the boy. "Do you really think that milk can make me grow?"

"Milk and all the other good food you must take. But there are other things you must also do. You must not run about so much, and you must not ride so hard every day. One can't put flesh on a boy who is constantly running, who never stands still a minute! Why, Fernando, you are just like a—like a big flea, jumping all over the castle! One can never put a finger on you."

His mother looked so wide-eyed and dismayed when she said this that Fernando had to laugh. But he stopped suddenly. Did he really look like a big flea? He could not be very attractive to others.

"Also, every day before dinner, you must rest in your room for half an hour," went on Doña Tereza, firmly.

"Me? Rest?" cried Fernando, indignantly.

"Certainly. The reason that you can't eat your dinner is that you come to the table all tired out. Now, if you promise to do these things, I will go to old Anna, who keeps the herb garden. She will mix a brew from the herbs which will make you *wish* to eat."

"Can you promise surely that all this will make me grow?"

"Of course it will. And besides, it will be a lovely joke on Sir Juan as he sees you getting taller and fatter. You will tell him nothing of all this. It shall be a secret between us. We shall not even tell your father. Then one day Sir Juan will look at you and will say . . ." Here Doña Tereza lowered her pretty voice, trying to make it sound like a deep growl. " 'What's happened to you, Fernando? You look like a different boy!' "

She sounded so much like the big knight that Fernando rolled on the floor in laughter. Then he got up and hugged her.

"Mother, you are wonderful! It will be such a great joke on Sir Juan!"

He had started for the door on a run, but his

mother called to him sharply. Surprised, he had
stopped short, turning to look at her.

"You promised not to run! Begin now to fulfill
your promises," she said sternly. "You will walk
quietly out of this room and down the stairs—as a
true knight would walk and not just as a wild boy on
the run!"

"Yes, Mother," answered Fernando meekly,
moving slowly toward the door.

Now, as he walked up the hill in the early morning, Fernando was going over all this in his mind and
smiling. Suddenly a thought struck him. The smile
faded from his lips. Only yesterday he had promised
his mother not to run! But only a few moments ago,
he had raced from the castle and through the courtyard like a wild horse, completely forgetting his
promise. He sighed heavily. It was going to be hard
to remember all the things he had promised—all the
things which would help him to become a strong
knight. But he *would* remember them! He *must!*

Resolutely he pushed on again. He had reached
the summit of the hill and had come out upon a large
square. There, facing him, stood the cathedral of
Lisbon, a great pile of rough stone, with a cross
above, and a bell tower at the side. He quickened
his pace. Good! He was in time. He had wanted to
get there before the bell began calling the people to
early Mass.

Slipping into the cool shadows of the church, he
found it empty. He knelt and blessed himself and

moved toward the high altar. There he dropped to his knees on the broad stone step which faced the tabernacle. This was Fernando's favorite place of prayer, and he liked it best when there was no one about.

The step felt cool and strong beneath his knees. Looking upward, he prayed earnestly for the grace to remember all his promises and for strength to fulfill them. Last of all he prayed that if it should be God's will, he would become a great knight, and would fight in a crusade, and would win many infidels to God.

The prayer finished, he entered the sacristy to don the robe which he wore when serving at early Mass. When Fernando was very young he had been trained to serve at Mass, for his uncle, an older brother of Doña Tereza's, was canon of the cathedral. That meant that he was in charge of it and held a position above that of the other priests.

At Castle de Bulhom almost everyone attended daily Mass except Sir Juan and the men-at-arms who might be needed suddenly should any disturbance arise in the city. When the great bell in the cathedral tower began to toll, Fernando was ready. He could hear the people moving into the church. His mother and father would be there, and they would watch every move he made, would hear every response, so he must keep his mind on his task.

After Mass, he found his parents waiting for him as usual at the cathedral doors.

"God's morning, Mother and Father!" cried Fernando gaily.

"God's morning, son. You were up early today," smiled Doña Tereza as the three started down the hill.

Fernando remembered that it was at this point that he always broke into a run. It was such fun to run downhill and be the first to reach the castle! But he recalled his promise and, making a strong effort, he fell into a quiet walk beside his father. His mother gave him a flashing smile. She, too, had remembered.

Fernando looked up at his handsome father and reflected that he should be proud to walk at his side. Don Martinho was not quite so tall as Sir Juan, but he was broad of shoulder and strongly built, and his flashing, dark eyes looked out fearlessly above a straight nose and a firm mouth. He looked what he was—the chief magistrate of Lisbon who enforced law and order in the city. Fernando was very proud of him.

"I shall need you today, Fernando," said his father. "We shall ride out to inspect the lands which lie along the Tagus River. It's time to see how the serfs are getting along and to look into their needs, and also to see how they are handling the crops."

"Yes, Father," said Fernando.

"Be ready immediately after breakfast. It will be a long day's ride."

"I hope not too long," murmured Doña Tereza,

looking up at the sky, "for it seems that we shall have a very hot day."

"That may be," answered her husband, "but it is time that Fernando began seriously to learn the business of the estate. After all, he will be master of it some day, and he must learn how to govern it well."

Fernando felt his heart sink. The estate was very large; the farm lands along the Tagus covered many acres. They were part of the dowry his mother had brought from the House of Tavera when she had married his father. Were he to become a crusader, how on earth would he be able to manage the farms and the Castle de Bulhom besides?

"My son," went on Don Martinho seriously, "it is time that you left off the things of a boy and began to take on those of a man. Some day you will be very rich, perhaps the richest man in all Portugal. I have spent my life that this should be so. But riches carry responsibilities. You must learn to assume them. You must learn to be a wise and a just governor, to be mindful of the rights of the poor, and, at the same time, to protect your estate."

"Yes, Father," replied Fernando meekly. But within him his heart rebelled. He did not wish to be a rich man. He wanted only to be a knight and to ride on a crusade.

"You have done very well with the accounts of the castle," went on his father. "The cathedral school will soon open again when this heat has passed. You will return and apply yourself seriously to your studies. The more you learn, the better you will handle the property that will one day be yours."

"Yes, Father," murmured Fernando again, his heart sinking lower and lower. All his dreams of becoming a squire this year were crashing. But he knew that this was not the moment to raise the question. He must have time to think up a good argument. His father would be angry, but he believed that his mother would stand with him, now that they had their secret. And Fernando had observed that Doña Tereza could usually get his father to do almost anything she desired. If he kept all his promises, and grew strong and tall, his mother would persuade his father to send him off as a squire.

Now, as the three walked down the hill, all at once they heard the sound of horses below them and men shouting. They looked down to see the mounted knights and the men-at-arms pouring out of the passage and taking the road to the city at a gallop.

"Trouble," said Don Martinho, hastening his pace.

Just then Sir Juan galloped up with the sun glinting on his armor. He pulled up his great black horse and cried, "Rioting at the port! One of our vessels captured a pirate ship. They killed all the Moors aboard and brought her in. She was heavy with booty, but when they began to unload her, every ruffian along the shore fell on them to grab the gold. There's a rare fight on, and we're off!"

"Take all the villains you can lay your hands on and lock them up. I'll be right there!" cried Don Martinho, starting at a run for the stables.

Sir Juan wheeled his horse sharply on the stones, making the sparks fly, and was off at a gallop. Fernando was running along at his father's side.

"I'm coming, too!" he cried.

Don Martinho stopped short and caught the boy by the shoulder.

"No!" he cried angrily, his eyes flashing. "You will stay here! This is a man's business! You stay away from the port until you are grown. Do you hear me?" And, roughly shoving his son aside, he threw his leg over the horse a groom had brought and was off like the wind.

Fernando stood there, his head down and his heart breaking. He felt his mother's light touch on his arm.

"Come, son," she said gently. "Patience, patience! All will come right in time if we only wait to learn God's will. Come, let us go in to breakfast. Your poor father had to ride away without it."

How hard it was to be only thirteen, Fernando thought, as he followed her through the passage and into the silent, deserted courtyard. Then Jingo, his black and white spotted hound, ran out from the stables and up to his master. He rubbed his nose against Fernando's leg as though to say he understood.

Chapter Three

PEDRO AND SANCHO

THE schoolroom was part of the cathedral, opening out upon a garden at the rear where bright flowers of red and yellow bloomed. Here the boys were allowed to play when school was over. Out they would run through the low stone door to climb the trees, to chase one another through the thick bushes, and to toss balls across the wall which separated the garden from the fields.

On a warm day in September, not many weeks

after his father and Sir Juan had brought order at the port and had punished the rioters, Fernando sat on a low bench which ran all the way along the walls of the schoolroom. A dozen or more boys sat there with him. They were the sons of the knights and merchants of Lisbon.

At the end of the room, raised upon a dais, stood the teacher's chair. Fernando's uncle, the gentle, white-haired Canon Rodriguez, was giving a lesson in history.

Fernando sat between Pedro and Sancho. They had been late that morning, arriving breathless just as the lesson began. They were twin brothers of about the same age as he, and had red hair and wide, smiling mouths. They looked so much alike that Fernando could scarcely tell them apart, except that Pedro had more freckles than Sancho. They were the sons of the blacksmith who kept his forge just outside the walls of Castle de Bulhom but who lived with his children and his red-haired French wife down at the port.

They did not have as fine clothes as the other boys, and everyone knew that their father was poor, but Fernando liked them better than all the others. They were lively and funny and had wonderful stories to tell about their adventures at the port.

They told of the strange ships that came sailing into the harbor and of the men from faraway lands who walked ashore. Some were very tall, they said, with such white skins and fair hair as you had never seen in Portugal. They wore outlandish clothing and came from an island kingdom which lay far to the north. They were called Angles. Pedro and Sancho laughed much as they spoke of the strangers' efforts to speak the language of Portugal and of how the boys at the port played tricks on them. Pedro would imitate the strangers' dismay, causing Fernando to go off into peals of laughter. But they said all agreed that the Angles were brave and could handle a ship as well as any Portuguese.

Often, too, they told tales of Old Lopez, a mysterious fisherman who had built his house far down the beach. He owned a large sailing vessel which carried a crew of four. Pedro and Sancho said that his crew was made up of the worst ruffians at the port. Among the older people it was whispered that the mother of Old Lopez had been a Moor.

"He is gone on his ship for many weeks at a time," explained Pedro, "and when he returns, it is always at night so that no one ever sees what he brings back."

"He speaks very little to others," said Sancho, "but we are sure that he must have had some wonderful adventures. We hope to get him to tell us about them someday!"

From that moment Fernando had desired with all his heart to meet Old Lopez. He was thinking about it now as he sat there quietly in the schoolroom between the twins while Canon Rodriguez was talking about the early history of Lisbon.

"Lisbon was once called Ulisbona," he was explaining, "because it is said that many centuries ago it was built by the Greek hero Ulysses who, as you know, wandered for many years far from his homeland. But nearer to our time Lisbon, and all that is now Portugal, lay under the rule of the infidels, the conquering Moors. They held the land for 400 years until Spain, aided by France, finally liberated it, driving out the infidel and restoring Christianity."

The boys on the bench stirred restlessly. It was a fine September day, and they were thinking of the garden.

"But it was a little more than fifty years ago," went on their teacher, "when Portugal at last became an independent kingdom under Alphonso I. The ancestors of many of you fought gloriously in the long crusades against the Moors."

The canon paused and could not help smiling at his nephew. But for once Fernando's thoughts were not upon crusades. Pedro had just whispered to him, "Meet us in the garden after school. Exciting news! Old Lopez . . ."

At a warning glance from the canon, Pedro had subsided. Fernando felt that he could not wait until school was out. Dimly he heard his uncle's voice saying, "Ever since that time, the Christian land of Portugal, and the city of Lisbon, have prospered. Into the River Tagus, into the port, have flowed the wealth of Europe and the Indies."

When at last classes were over, Fernando, for all

his eagerness to reach the garden, hurried first through the corridor which connected the schoolroom with the church to make the quick afternoon prayer he always made at that time. As he emerged, his uncle was just entering the cathedral.

Canon Rodriguez stopped the boy a moment to say, "It is well to pray, Fernando. You must never forget that, upon your birth, your good mother, my sister, consecrated you to the Mother of God. She wants you always to continue in that devotion. You must ask our Lady to keep you pure and good. You must ask her to pray to God to deliver you from all evil."

"Yes, uncle," smiled Fernando. Then he made off quickly to join his friends in the garden. Pedro grasped his arm excitedly, eyes dancing.

"We met Old Lopez yesterday on our way home from school! He was very pleasant and invited us to sit down and talk with him. We sat on the rocks not far from his house. And what do you think?" Pedro paused dramatically. "He wants to meet you!"

Fernando's eyes opened wide. "Me?" he asked in astonishment.

"Yes," said Sancho, dancing up and down. "He wants to help you become a knight!"

"But how . . ." began Fernando.

Pedro interrupted him. "We told Old Lopez all about you and how you want to go out as a squire, become a knight, and fight in a crusade!"

"He said that it was too bad that your father and Sir Juan were making you wait," explained Sancho. "He will be glad to help you if we will bring you to see him tomorrow afternoon after school!"

"But how can he help me?" asked the puzzled Fernando.

Pedro airily waved an arm. "Oh," he said, "Old Lopez knows very important people all over the world—people who need squires and things. He has powerful friends in almost every land. He's been everywhere and has had *such* adventures! You should hear him!"

"Has he been to the Holy Land?" eagerly asked Fernando.

"He did not say so," said Pedro, "but I should not be surprised if he had."

"He said it was silly for you to wait longer before becoming a squire," explained Sancho. "He will tell you how it can be done in no time at all. So you will come with us tomorrow?"

"Oh, yes!" cried Fernando delightedly, with shining eyes.

"And he said that he might even show us the inside of his house and some of the treasures he has brought home from his journeys!" went on Pedro, excitedly. "But he made us promise that we would not tell anyone that we were meeting him. And he asked you to promise, too."

"I promise," quickly said Fernando.

"We'll set off right after school," said Sancho.

"People won't know where we're going. They'll just think we're walking down the hill together."

"And we can branch off on the little path which runs at the back of the castle," went on Pedro, "so that no one will see you."

And so it was agreed between the three.

At dinner that night in the great hall, Fernando sat next to his mother and across from his father and Sir Juan.

"We may have trouble at the port again," observed Sir Juan, frowning. "The fishing has been poor and the people are hungry. And when they are hungry, they are in a mood for riot."

"Can we not send food to them, husband?" quickly asked Doña Tereza, her big eyes looking earnestly at Don Martinho.

"We've been sending food every day," grumbled her husband. "But try as we may, as soon as our backs are turned, the stronger will fall upon the weaker and snatch all for themselves. Those water rats . . ." His face grew livid with anger. "They see to it that little reaches the old, the sick and the very poor!"

He saw his wife's eyes fill with tears, and he said in a softer tone:

"Do not grieve, wife. You forget that there are the good Augustinian fathers with their monastery just outside the city walls. Daily they dispense food to the poor. The monastery is rich, so they can afford it. Anyone who is really hungry can always get food from the holy priest who serves as guest master."

Doña Tereza was smiling again.

"They are holy and learned men," she nodded, "those canons of St. Augustine. There are no greater scholars in all the land and none who preach so well!"

"But the whole port needs a good cleaning out," went on Don Martinho with a frown. "I'd like to sweep it clean of the water rats! I often wonder where some of them came from. Many are not Portuguese at all. They are riffraff from all over the world who have settled at our port because they have heard that Lisbon is a rich city and they hope to make a dishonest living here. I even suspect that some have been, or still are, pirates and that they sneak out in their boats at night to rob and do murder on the high seas!"

With his clenched fist he struck the oaken table a blow so hard that the silver goblets trembled and one overturned, spilling its red wine across the board.

"By the sword of my ancestors," he cried, "I will yet sweep the port clean of them!"

When Fernando went to bed that night he was troubled. More than ever did he wish to visit the port and see for himself all the things of which his father had spoken. More than ever did he want to meet Old Lopez who would help him become a knight! But he recalled that day in midsummer when his father and Sir Juan had ridden forth to quell the riot and when his father had said to him sternly, "You stay away from the port until you are grown!"

Well, it could be said truthfully that he *had* grown, though perhaps not much. That had been almost three months ago. He had remembered his promises to his mother. He had eaten everything that she had put before him. He had even taken the milk in the forenoon and the afternoon. He had faithfully sipped the bitter brew which old Anna made from the herbs. He recalled, not without some pride, how every day he had gone to his room to rest a half hour before dinner. That had been the hardest thing of all! Yet he had done it. And he had certainly curbed his running about and the long, hard rides on his horse.

And to his great pleasure, he had learned that his mother had been right. Mother usually *was* right, he reflected. He had put on weight; his doublet no longer hung loosely on his shoulders. Then had come that wonderful day when Sir Juan had measured Fernando's length against the old mark on the armory wall, which recorded his height as it had been in July. In September, Sir Juan had been able to place the new mark a whole inch higher! He had given Fernando a hearty thump on the back and had cried in surprise, "Lad, you are growing!"

What a good joke that had been on Sir Juan! And how his mother and he had secretly laughed over it!

He *had* grown and he *was* growing. He tried to tell himself that this new growth had released him from his father's command. But what exactly had his father meant when he had said, ". . . until you are *grown?*" A persistent, quiet voice within him kept asking: "Are you sure you are not cheating?"

Perhaps he should ask his father's consent before visiting the port tomorrow with Pedro and Sancho. But no, he could not do that, for he had promised the twins not to tell anyone of their plan. And had not Sir Juan always taught him that a true knight never broke his promise?

He tossed from side to side, unable to sleep. It was all very confusing. Would he break his promise to his friends, tell his father, and risk refusal to visit the port? Or would he go secretly down the hill with Pedro and Sancho to learn how quickly he could become a knight? These were such hard problems to solve! Was all life going to be this way? Was it to be filled with questions to which there would be at least two quite different and opposing answers? Fernando turned over on his pillow, sighed, and at last fell asleep.

He dreamed that he was a knight in shining armor, mounted on a white charger and leading an army before which the walls of Jerusalem were falling.

Chapter Four

Sign of Evil

WHEN on the next afternoon the three boys reached the port, Fernando thought that he had never seen anything so exciting. There was a market square laid out at one side, where all sorts of things were displayed. But the boys were far more interested in the water front.

There the fishermen were busy emptying their nets of live fish which were flopping about everywhere. Small boats were beached nearby. Out upon the water, larger boats, many of which carried sails of brilliant colors, red and blue and yellow, drifted with the wind. Farther out lay even larger ships, riding at anchor. And everywhere the blue water sparkled in the bright sun and the white gulls circled above it.

Jingo frolicked along at Fernando's side. He had met them at the spot where the road forked off on the little path which skirted the back of the castle. Every day this was where he waited for his master to return from school. He was enjoying the excitement of the port as much as the boys.

"Look!" pointed Pedro. "That big ship has come all the way from Angle Land. You can tell from the flag. Perhaps we shall meet some of those tall, funny men. If so, I shall get them to speak and you will laugh."

Fernando gazed out at the busy harbor. The larger ships had square holes which ran all along their hulls and from which long oars extended.

"Those," explained Sancho, "are for rowing the ship when the wind fails. Slaves sit on benches behind those holes and push the ship along with their strokes. The slaves are chained to the benches, and a man walks up and down between them, carrying a great whip to use on their backs if they grow lazy!"

"How awful!" exclaimed Fernando. "But just the same I should like to be the captain of such a ship and sail far away to strange lands."

"So should I!" cried the other two.

"Some day I shall sail on such a ship to the Holy Land," added Fernando confidently.

As they made their way down the crowded, noisy road which ran above the beach, they had to dodge in and out between the carts and the donkeys, between rough sailors with heavy beards, and between bronzed fishermen. Many of them were quarreling in loud voices and swearing at one another—strange oaths which Fernando had never heard before. All carried daggers and knives stuck into their wide belts. Some—and he judged these to be officers—carried swords.

He was glad when they got away from the crowd and began to walk down the beach toward the rocks where Old Lopez had said he would meet them. At last the spot came in view, and there, sure enough, perched on a big boulder above the sea, sat a strange figure of a man. Jingo ran up to him and sniffed curiously.

"Sir, this is Fernando, the son of the chief magistrate," said Pedro respectfully when they came up to him.

Old Lopez looked down at the three and grinned at them from a mouth which seemed to hold only two yellowed teeth.

"Welcome, mates!" he rumbled in a hoarse voice.

Fernando stared up at him, fascinated. He was a great square of a man, with a huge head sunk between his shoulders and a thick crop of white hair. It made a strange contrast with his face, which was burned almost black from the sun and was full of deep furrows. Above one eye there ran a scar which caused the eyelid to droop so that at first one thought that Old Lopez was constantly winking.

"So this is the lad who wants to become a knight?" he boomed, looking Fernando up and down from his head to his toes.

"Yes, sir, please," said Fernando politely, drawing himself up to his full height.

"Well, now, that should not be difficult," replied the other, "if you will do exactly what Old Lopez tells you to do." He turned to Pedro and Sancho. "And you, also!" he exclaimed.

The red-haired twins looked rather surprised. They had not thought that they were in on this at all.

"Come and sit up here beside me, mates." Old Lopez patted the rock, and up the three scrambled. Jingo made it in one bound.

"Now look out there," continued the old man, pointing over the water. They followed his finger with their eyes and saw, riding gracefully on the waves, a fair-sized ship with a black hull and with all her sails furled.

"That's my ship at anchor, the good *San Diabolo*," he said proudly. "And no faster sloop sails anywhere in all the world!"

The boys strained their eyes to see better.

"Now, how would you three lads like to sail away on her tonight with Old Lopez and his crew?"

The boys looked at him, astonished. He leaned

forward and lowered his voice, as though he were telling them a great secret.

"I have need of some lively cabin boys," he said, "and you will have a wonderful journey! We shall touch at many strange ports. Then we shall sail on to the land of France . . ." Here he turned to Fernando. "And there, my lad, you shall become squire to a great lord who is a friend of mine. He will be organizing a crusade. You shall go with him to the Holy Land, and he will make you a knight upon the field of battle!"

"Oh!" exclaimed Fernando, drawing in his breath and opening his eyes wide. It seemed too wonderful to be true. But then almost at once he thought of his father.

"This is very kind of you, sir," he said, "but must we really sail tonight? You see," he added sadly, "I am afraid my father will not give his consent."

Old Lopez threw back his head in a roar of laughter.

"Your father! But surely, lad, you would not be so foolish as to tell your father? Why, lads of your age make their own decisions!" Then his voice grew stern and he leaned forward, looking into the face of each. They drew back, and Jingo uttered a low growl.

"Remember, I want no babies on the *San Diabolo!*" he exclaimed. "I will have only brave lads about me, for they will be sailing with brave men!" Then he drew back and grinned again. "The great sights you shall see!" he continued. "We shall touch first at Morocco . . ."

"Morocco!" broke in Pedro. "But that's the Moorish country, and the Moors are our enemies. They would kill us all, or make slaves of us!"

Old Lopez swelled out his chest and looked down at him disdainfully.

"Not when you sail with Old Lopez on the *San Diabolo,*" he said. "I have good friends in Morocco. They know me and my vessel. And it happens that I do quite a lot of business there."

Again he leaned forward, whispering, "You will all come back with treasure stored in your sea chests!"

"Treasure!" exclaimed the boys in unison.

"Now, all that you have to do, mates," the old man went on in an easier tone, "is, first of all, not to speak of this to *anyone!* Not a murmur out of one of you, or the plan will fail! Next, you must lie awake tonight until you are sure that everyone else is fast asleep. Then, creep softly out into the night and meet me here. Bring nothing with you. Old Lopez will provide you with all that you may need."

He turned to Fernando.

"You," he said, "may have to climb the castle wall when the sentry isn't looking."

"Oh, I can do that all right!' exclaimed Fernando, his eyes dancing with excitement. "I know just the place!" Then he thought for a moment. "But, sir . . ." he hesitated.

"But what?" roared Old Lopez.

"It's awfully kind of you, sir, and we do appreciate it," said Fernando, "but I was just wondering whether I could leave a note for my father? You see, I shall be gone so long—on the crusade and everything."

"No notes!" cried the old man. "That would spoil everything. They would be after you like an arrow. They might even catch you before we could get our sails raised and into the wind!" He stood up and stretched.

"Now come. I will show you some of the fine things I have brought back from just such journeys —such things as you, yourselves, shall bring back!"

Considering his age, it was surprising how fast Old Lopez scrambled down the rock, thought Fernando. When he started toward his house, which was set back from the shore, the boys noticed that his strong legs were bowed outward and that, as he walked, he seemed to roll from side to side.

From the outside the house looked poor enough and small enough, but when they got inside, Fernando was surprised to see how richly furnished it was and how much larger than it had seemed. From the end of the long room where they stood, he could see a door, so there must be another room behind this one, he thought. Jingo trotted about, sniffing at everything.

Suddenly Fernando began to feel strangely uneasy. It was as though someone else were in the room with them—someone he could not see. Jingo came up to him and growled a little. Fernando reached down to quiet the dog and was surprised to find him trembling.

Against the wall there stood three large chests of carved wood. Old Lopez moved toward one and unlocked it with a giant key which hung from his belt. He turned to the boys and said, "These things I show only to my friends and my shipmates. You are to be both. You will not tell others about them because Old Lopez might then be robbed!"

With that, he flung open the lid. The boys stood there dazzled by an array of jewels and gold such as they had never seen before. The old man leaned down and picked up a handful of gems. He dropped them slowly from between his fingers, watching them glitter and sparkle in the light of the setting sun filtering through the window. His eyes shone happily.

"Are they not beautiful?" he asked, smiling. "Such things you, too, shall bring back from our voyage!"

He looked at Pedro and Sancho.

"You, who have always been poor, will return as rich men."

Then he said to Fernando, "And you will return as a great knight!"

The boys stood there gaping. But now again Fernando had the uneasy feeling that they were not alone. Someone else was there, watching and smiling—someone who was invisible. Jingo was whining at his feet. But the twins, wide-eyed and interested, had not seemed to notice anything. All at once Fernando was afraid.

Old Lopez closed the chest and locked it.

"And now," he said, moving toward a table, "you have but to sign this parchment, promising to sail tonight on the good ship *San Diabolo*."

He picked up a parchment and a quill from the table. "It is rather a ceremony," he said as he moved toward the door at the end of the room. "This parchment is always signed before the likeness of my master."

"Your master?" asked Pedro, surprised.

"He will soon be your master, too," answered Old Lopez. "He is good to me and will be good to you. He brings riches and power to all who sign in his service!"

At that he flung open the door and pushed the boys into the room.

At first they could see nothing in the dark except a few candles which flared and blew their smoke as the door opened. The heavy smell of incense made them cough. Then gradually they were able to make out a figure of stone which sat high upon an altar at the end of the room. Candles and lamps flared redly at its feet. Incense burned before it. Jingo growled again, and Fernando looked down to see the dog tense, his hair standing on end. The boys peered through the gloom. All at once the air cleared, and the stone figure seemed to come to life. Fernando shook with fear because, while the face was smiling, above the forehead he could plainly see the outline of two small horns.

Old Lopez stood ready with the quill and parchment at a small table near the door.

"Make your mark here," he said pleasantly to the boys. "I'll just scratch your wrists lightly with my dagger, as it's customary to sign the paper in one's own blood."

Suddenly Fernando knew the smiling figure upon the altar as the Prince of all Evil. His spine turned to ice. He tried to move but could not. His feet seemed rooted to the floor.

"Come, my brave lads," urged Old Lopez. "It takes only a moment. And after that you will find that you are no longer boys but have become men!"

Unable to move, Fernando made a tremendous effort to pray. Then suddenly something freed him. He turned quickly and grasped at the trembling twins.

"Fly!" he cried. "This is the sign of all evil! Fly for your lives! Fly for your souls!"

The three frightened boys lurched for the door. Old Lopez held out his strong arms to stop them, but Jingo, with a long, low growl, bounded at his throat. At the same moment Pedro charged with his head at the big man's middle and knocked the wind from him. Before he had caught his breath, the boys and Jingo had raced from the house.

Pedro and Sancho flew for their home, far up the beach. Fernando ran like a hare up the hill, with Jingo beside him, toward the Castle de Bulhom. But when he got there, he did not stop. He kept on running until, breathless and exhausted, he reached the cathedral. Jingo, his tongue hanging out, dropped down panting on the doorsill. Fernando stumbled into the church and up the aisle, gasping and shaking.

He reached the low, stone step beneath the tabernacle. Sobbing, he flung himself upon it. At last he raised his head upward and saw the face of Christ looking down at him. He made the Sign of the Cross upon his forehead. And then, with shaking fingers, he traced it again upon the stone step where he knelt.

He did not know how long he stayed there in prayer. "Deliver us from all evil," he kept whispering. At length the shaking ceased and a great peace came upon him. Again he blessed himself and rose to go.

Something made him look down at the step where he had knelt. Upon it he saw, deeply imbedded in the hard stone, and as though cut there by a chisel, the Sign of the Cross he had just now traced there lightly with his trembling fingers.

Chapter Five

CROSS IN THE STONE

EARLY the next morning, when Canon Rodriguez was finishing his breakfast, he looked up to see Manuel making violent signs at him from the doorway. Manuel was a poor workman who lived nearby and who was both deaf and dumb. It was hard for him to earn a living, so the canon employed him to clean the church every morning after Mass. Now it was plain that Manuel was greatly disturbed about something.

Father Rodriguez rose and followed him into the church. Manuel led him to the step beneath the high altar, and, with shaking finger, pointed to the cross in the stone.

The canon stared down at it. Whence had it come? Certainly it had not been there yesterday! He knelt to examine it closer. Then he ran his finger along the smooth, deep grooves. A master workman had cut this. But how? And why? He knelt there thinking for a long moment. Then he turned to Manuel and motioned to him to come and kneel beside him. Together the two prayed silently in the empty church.

The canon decided to say nothing about the matter since he did not understand it. He knew that poor Manuel would not say anything, either. He could not, even if he wished to. It was likely that any others who might notice the cross would think that it had been there always. Meantime, he determined to visit the church more frequently during the day to observe more closely those who knelt upon that step.

There was another, too, who decided to say nothing about the cross, and that was Fernando. Fortunately, his visit to the port had not been discovered. When he had reached home that evening, the grooms in the courtyard were busy with the horses of a company of nobles and their ladies who had been invited to dine at Castle de Bulhom. Fernando had just time to reach his room, to wash his face and hands, comb his hair, and put on a fresh doublet before the guests began to gather in the great hall.

As he entered it and moved to join his mother and father, he hoped that his face did not betray the strange events of that afternoon.

"Why, son, you look very pale," said Doña Tereza anxiously, passing her hand lightly over his hair. "Didn't you rest tonight before dinner?"

Fernando forced a smile and whispered to her, "I was prevented. But this is the first time I've missed!"

She nodded approvingly and turned to her guests. His father, who was busy talking with a group of noblemen, took no notice of him. But Sir Juan strolled up and said, "You look as though you had been through the mill, young fellow!"

He eyed the lad curiously. Fernando shuffled his feet and looked down. He felt the color rising in his cheeks. It was hard to keep anything from Sir Juan. He seemed to be able to read a boy's mind.

"I was thirteen myself once," continued Sir Juan with a twinkle, "and was very busy trying to learn the mysteries of the world all at once. I know all about being thirteen. But next time you go adventuring, young man, you had better take me with you. I still enjoy fun, you know. I'm not ready for the grave yet!"

"All right," smiled Fernando. "Next time you shall come with me!" Then he added teasingly, "But this time it was better to have Jingo."

"Jingo!" exclaimed the knight. "So you prefer the company of a dog to mine? Now, that's a compliment. Can Jingo then protect you better than I?"

"Well, he did pretty well this afternoon," smiled Fernando mysteriously as he moved to take his place at the table.

That was all that had happened at home following the strangest and most frightening day of his life. Fernando sent up a prayer of thanksgiving. In going to the port he had disobeyed his father. He should have known that from the start. But his eagerness to meet Old Lopez had forced him to deceive himself.

He deserved the awful experience he had met. God had been very good, for it could have been so much worse. In spite of his folly, he had been rescued. Why, at this very moment he might have been in a rolling ship on the high seas, pledged with his own blood forever to serve the Prince of Evil! He shuddered. His hand shook, and he spilled some of the wine from his goblet.

"Steady, young fellow," whispered Sir Juan who was sitting next him. "These things are never as bad as they seem."

It was only when Fernando closed his door that night and was at last alone that he could think about that other part of the day's adventures. For some remarkable reason that he could not fathom, he, Fernando de Bulhom, had been granted a share in a secret with God! He would have to think about it, and think about it. He would have to think about it a lot! But he went to sleep with a light, and strangely happy, heart.

After school, in the garden, as the days passed, he and the twins held many whispered conversations about that terrible afternoon. But Fernando kept quiet about his experience in the cathedral.

At first Pedro and Sancho had been too frightened to go near the house of Old Lopez, although on the very next morning they had seen, sure enough, that his ship, the *San Diabolo*, had vanished. She had sailed away in the night. At last they drew courage to walk up the beach to his house. They reported to Fernando that they had peered in at the windows and had seen that it was completely empty. Old Lopez had taken his rich furnishings and the three treasure chests with him. They could not see into the back room, and they were glad.

"And may Old Lopez never return!" exclaimed Pedro.

"Amen," said Fernando and Sancho in one breath.

Early one morning a few weeks later, Don Martinho, who was busy with the king's messenger from Coimbra, sent Fernando and Sir Juan out to inspect the lands which lay along the Tagus. Fernando rode Panzo, his favorite horse, and Jingo trotted along at the rear. It was a clear morning and a fine ride, and nothing on the farms escaped the keen eye of Sir Juan. At the same time, his amusing comments caused Fernando to rock in the saddle with laughter.

Returning about midday, their road took them past the old monastery of San Vicente, which lay just outside the city walls. Fernando knew that it was the monastery of the Canons of St. Augustine, the monks of whose charity his father had so often spoken. The sprawling stone building, with its high walls and iron-studded gate, had been built by King Alphonso I during the siege of Lisbon.

As they rode up the hill, Sir Juan nodded toward it and said, "When your ancestors were fighting to redeem Lisbon, King Alphonso put the good monks there to pray that the crusaders would drive out the Moors."

"They must have prayed well!" exclaimed Fernando. "But I should think that they would much rather have been fighting in the siege. Still, I suppose that monks cannot fight."

"Oh, indeed they can!" declared Sir Juan.

Fernando looked at him in surprise.

"Mark you," went on Sir Juan, "I have known monks to fight as bravely and as staunchly as any knight!"

"How is that?" asked Fernando.

"There are always monks who accompany a crusade. They carry the cross to inspire the soldiers. They preach and administer the Sacraments to the wounded and the dying. Brave men they are, moving in the thick of battle, ministering to Christian and Saracen alike. But many a time, when the tide of battle has been going against us, I have seen these very monks doff their long robes to seize shield and spear and charge with the best of us!"

Fernando's eyes danced with delight.

"I should love to see that!" he exclaimed.

"No crusade was ever won yet without a good preacher in the midst," said Sir Juan thoughtfully.

They were riding past the rear of the building where the kitchens lay, and now Fernando saw a long line of people stretching up the road from the port, through the monastery gardens, and up to a door at one side. Most of them were old and in rags. Some were crippled, and all carried baskets.

"The poor, who come daily for their ration of food," observed Sir Juan.

Fernando drew in his horse.

"Let us stay and watch a little," he urged.

The knight pulled up beside him, and Jingo ran off to snuff around the garden, hoping to smell out a rabbit. The two riders watched the monk who stood at the door. He wore a white robe and smiled as he placed the bread in the outstretched baskets. He had a word and a blessing to give to each. He looked very happy, thought Fernando.

"He is the monastery's guest master," explained Sir Juan. "His task is not only to feed the poor, but also to receive all the visitors who come to the monastery."

"Oh, do let us help him now!" exclaimed Fernando impetuously.

"And risk your father's anger for being late? Not on your life!" exclaimed the knight, turning his horse. "Let the good monks alone! They have their work to do and we have ours."

So Fernando whistled to Jingo and set Panzo into a fast trot for home.

The weeks were passing quickly and, as Christmas drew near, Doña Tereza said one day to Fernando:

"We have been invited to spend the holidays at the Castle Almada as guests of Don Roberto and Doña Maria."

"Don Roberto?" asked Fernando excitedly, dropping the hunting knife he had been cleaning. "Do you mean that splendid nobleman who often rides here with his knights?"

Doña Tereza nodded. "He is the Duke of Almada, you know, and is very powerful with the king. He and your father are old friends. And Doña Maria and I have known each other since we were children."

"What fun!" exclaimed Fernando.

"There will be other guests, too," said his mother, "and boys and girls of your own age. You must take your best clothes and see that they are in good order. And above all, you must take your best *manners!*"

Fernando looked a little frightened. He had never before attended a house party.

"Will it be very stiff and formal?" he asked.

"Not too much so," said his mother soothingly, "but you must remember that you are growing up now and should learn how to behave in the presence of ladies and knights. You must also learn to dance a little."

"Dance!" exclaimed Fernando in horror.

Doña Tereza nodded firmly. "I have engaged a dancing master to give you lessons during the next few weeks."

"But I had planned to go hunting with Sir Juan!" objected Fernando.

"You must give that up for the time."

Her son looked so dismayed that Doña Tereza had to laugh. She leaned over and patted his hand.

"Don't look so sad," she said. "There will be hunting also at Castle Almada!"

He brightened up at once. And while he did not like the dancing lessons a bit, to please his mother he tried his best at them during the time that followed. After all, he could look forward to the hunting and also to another good thing. He had learned that Sir Juan would accompany them to Castle Almada.

With his knights and his retainers, Don Martinho's company made almost thirty as they rode through the December countryside. They reached the great gates of Almada at sunset.

Don Roberto and Doña Maria waited to greet them, smiling and extending hands of welcome. Beside them stood their three children: Jaime, a lad of fifteen, and his sisters, Isabella and Inez. Fernando liked Jaime at once. He was fat and jolly, with merry brown eyes and a mouth that was always turned up at the corners. Fernando greeted the girls shyly. He could see that Isabella, who was thirteen, was very pretty. Inez, who was only eleven, smiled up at him out of deep blue eyes and a thin little face. For a moment he did not notice that she was on crutches.

The great hall rang with merriment that night, and after dinner there was dancing. Fernando had enjoyed himself hugely with the other boys at dinner. They were six in all, including Jaime, and they had talked of the hunting they would do tomorrow, and of becoming squires, for all desired to be knights and to follow the crusades.

Two were of the same age as Fernando, and he was glad to see that they were only a little taller than he. He told himself happily that he *had* grown during these past months, but Sir Juan still said that he was too thin. He wished that he could grow fat, like Jaime, who sat at the head of the table and kept saying funny things to everyone. By the time dinner was ended, the boys were all good friends.

But the dancing was different. All at once Fernando's stomach felt very queer. He knew that he was supposed to ask Isabella to dance, but it took all his courage to do so. She was indeed pretty, but she frightened him. She seemed so grownup, and proud—and, yes, *stuffy!* But he got through it somehow. As they danced, he saw little Inez sitting, her crutches at her side, watching them delightedly. Her thin little face was all smiles, and she was clapping her hands in time to the music. He wondered how she could be so happy. She was the only girl there not able to dance, and all the others were greatly enjoying themselves.

The grownups were dancing, too, and Fernando could see that Sir Juan was having a wonderful time. Once, when the music stopped for a little, the knight strolled over to him.

"How's it going, young fellow?" he asked in a low tone.

"The boys are fine," whispered Fernando. "But the girls . . ."

"What's the matter with the girls?" asked Sir Juan.

"I—I just don't know what to say to them!" exclaimed Fernando miserably.

"That's easy. When you can't think of anything to say, just tell them how pretty they are. That always works," said the knight, as he strolled away.

The next morning Jaime took Fernando out to the stables to show him the horses.

"This is Carlo, my good hunter," he said, patting the neck of a large brown horse with long legs. "He is very fast."

"Panzo and I will be glad to race you and him!" cried Fernando eagerly.

"Good! Tomorrow, for today we go hunting,"

smiled Jaime. "I only hope the girls won't want to tag along," he added. "They would just be in the way. Isabella likes to hunt, but of course poor little Inez . . ."

"I'm so sorry about Inez," said Fernando.

For once Jaime looked sad. "When she was a little thing, she ran out into the courtyard when no one was looking, and a horse trampled on her. They say that she will always have to use crutches."

Fernando felt deeply sorry. All he could say was, "Well, Inez *looks* very happy in any case."

The six boys had a fine hunt and, much to the relief of Jaime and Fernando, the girls had not asked to be taken along. When they returned in the late afternoon, they found Inez wrapped in a warm cloak and sitting on the castle steps. As they came up to her, full of high spirits from their long ride, Fernando stopped to say, "I hope that you, too, have had a pleasant day, Inez."

She nodded with a gay, happy smile.

"I was waiting to see you," she said shyly. "I wanted to show you something—that is, that is—if you'd like to see it?"

"That's very nice of you," said Fernando. "What is it?"

"I wondered—I thought that perhaps—" she hesitated.

"Yes?" encouraged Fernando.

Inez plunged.

"Would you like to see our chapel?" she asked.

"I'd love to!" exclaimed Fernando with a smile. "You mean there is a chapel in the castle?"

Inez nodded as she took up her crutches. Fernando helped her to rise.

"This way," she said when they were inside. She led him down a long corridor which branched off to the left. Fernando, following the small figure, thought it was amazing how fast she got along on her crutches. Again he wondered at her happy spirit. At length they came to a door. Inez paused and turned to him, a finger at her lips.

"Here is where my greatest Friend lives," she whispered.

It was a lovely little stone chapel, with the light coming softly through its high, stained-glass windows. To Fernando's surprise, Inez did not move toward the high altar but, bowing her head before it, led him instead to a small shrine near it. There, in a niche, with a little lamp burning, stood a statue of the Child Jesus. It was carved in stone, and on its head there rested a small, golden crown. The head was beautiful, thought Fernando, and he marveled at the skill with which the sculptor had carved the features, and the softness of the smile.

Before it stood a low bench with a cushion and, as Inez could not very well kneel, she sat upon it and motioned Fernando to sit beside her. Lowering her head, she began silently to pray. Everything was very still. Fernando watched the light from the lamp as it flickered and glowed on the small golden-crowned figure before them. Then he, too, began to pray. After a while he seemed to hear a voice within him which said:

"Here is the secret of Inez's happiness."

When they had left the chapel and had closed the door behind them, she said to him:

"My father had the statue made especially for me after—after my accident. He said that he wanted me to have a very special Friend of my own and that the Child Jesus would take good care of me and understand as no grownups could."

"And he was right?" asked Fernando.

Now it seemed that all of Inez's face was smiling.

"Oh, yes!" she exclaimed. "It's wonderful what He does for me!"

"And that is why you do not mind your crutches?" asked Fernando softly.

"I hated them at first, but He has taught me to love them," she replied simply.

As they moved again down the long corridor, she went on:

"After I met you yesterday and then went in to visit Him, as I do every evening, it seemed that He was trying to tell me to bring you also to visit Him."

Fernando did not know what to say.

"So I've wanted to ask you," continued Inez, "to make Him your Friend also. You see, He too is a Boy, and understands boys." She stopped and looked up at him seriously. "Please promise me,

Fernando, that you will make Him your Friend, for I am sure that would please Him greatly."

"I promise," said Fernando, looking down into the earnest blue eyes.

The gay house party at Castle Almada ended shortly after the New Year began. In the months following his return home, Fernando found himself extremely busy. At school Canon Rodriguez was pushing him along rapidly in Latin and grammar, which demanded a great deal of study. There was also a class in rhetoric, in which the boys were compelled to stand up before the others and speak on some prepared subject. Fernando found it very embarrassing.

His father, too, was exacting more work of him on the accounts and in supervising the farms along the Tagus. Fernando would not have minded it all so much except that his social life kept interfering. He had made new friends at Castle Almada, and now they were forever riding over to invite him to parties at their homes. It soon became evident that all the young people wanted Fernando with them, whatever they were doing. He enjoyed their companionship and had even come to like dancing.

"I wish he would settle down and be serious," grumbled Don Martinho one evening to his wife. "He has much to learn before he will be able to manage this estate!"

Doña Tereza said nothing but only smiled quietly as she bent over her embroidery.

Between everything, Fernando found it hard to find time for his prayers there on the step with the cross in the stone. But somehow he managed it and, true to his promise to Inez, he had already made a special Friend of the Child Jesus. Every day he asked Him for help in becoming a knight and a crusader. Neither did he forget to pray for his parents and for little Inez. But he never guessed how often his uncle, the canon, slipping quietly into the church, saw him there at prayer.

Another August rolled around and, upon his fourteenth birthday, his father gave him a new dagger which had been fashioned in Toledo. It had a beautifully engraved hilt. Fernando was very proud of it and wore it constantly in his belt. He hoped that the gift was a sign that his father now considered him grown and would listen more patiently when the time came to ask that he be sent away as a squire. But Sir Juan still insisted that it was too soon. It was hard to be patient, but he was sure that the Christ Child was helping him as He had helped little Inez.

About six months after his birthday, he felt that he could wait no longer. It was time that he knew what he was going to do in life. He determined to make a special effort at prayer that the path to knighthood would be made clear. And he remembered how Sir Juan had told him of the vigils which were kept by certain knights when they wanted some special favor. A knight would lay his sword upon the altar, offering it to God, and would remain there in prayer all night long.

Well, he could hardly do that. First of all, not yet being knighted, he did not have the right to wear a sword or call one his own. But he could lay his new dagger on the altar and offer it to God. Next, he could hardly stay out all night without having his father and the entire castle at his heels. But he could slip away in the evening after dinner and would not be missed if he returned before ten o'clock. Thus he determined to keep his own sort of vigil.

On that cold, February evening there was no one in the cathedral when he slipped inside. He had given his dagger a special polishing that day, and now he tiptoed up to the altar and laid it there. All was quiet and dark in the church.

Unheeded, the hours passed as he knelt there, praying on the step with the cross in the stone. At last he arose, and suddenly he felt as though a great weight had been lifted from him. The way that for long had seemed so dark, shrouded by clouds, was suddenly illumined as by the midday sun of a summer day. He hastened down the aisle. He had forgotten all about his dagger. When he emerged in the dark on the steps of the cathedral, he was startled to feel a touch upon his arm.

"It is only I," said the voice of Canon Rodriguez. "So, Fernando, like any knight you have been keeping a vigil?"

He could not see his nephew's face in the dark, but he knew from the happy voice that the lad was smiling. Never before had that voice sounded so happy.

"At last I know what I am to do with my life!" Fernando exclaimed.

"I have known that for a very long time," said his uncle gently. "I was aware of it long before you were."

"Tell me, uncle, do you think that the good Father Prior will receive me into the monastery of San Vicente?" asked Fernando eagerly.

Chapter Six

Son of the Governor

ONE day in the early spring, little more than a year later, the young novice, Fernando, was busy with a hoe in the monastery garden. He was turning up the earth around some cabbages when he heard Brother Philippo calling to him.

"Father Fernando," came the voice, "Father Prior asks that you come to his office at once."

Fernando straightened his back and waved smilingly to the messenger. It always bothered him a little when the brothers called him "Father Fernando," for he had not yet been ordained a priest. He had been living in the monastery only since August, having been compelled to wait six months before he was accepted. But the brothers, who did not come to San Vicente to become priests, but only to serve the monastery, usually called the novices "Father" even before they were ordained.

Dropping the hoe, Fernando hastened toward Father Prior's office. As he hurried up the path, he thought with a smile that his mother, had she been there, would have been glad to see that he was not running. He could not very well run these days, for the long, black robe he wore got in the way.

He was also wondering why Father Prior had sent for him, and he was a little worried. Had he done anything wrong? He could not remember that he had, but then there were so many rules to keep in mind, it could easily be that he had forgotten one of them. But there was one thing about Father Prior, he thought. He was always kind and merry with the novices and never corrected them. He left that to the novice master. In fact, whenever you saw Father Prior he left you feeling that more than ever did you want to become a good monk. Fernando knocked gently at the door.

"Come in!" called the hearty voice which by now Fernando knew so well.

When he entered, the prior was seated at a large desk littered with parchments, quills, and inkpots.

He was a big man, broad-shouldered and white-haired, with deep eyes twinkling under bushy eyebrows, and a ready smile.

"Sit here, Fernando," he said, motioning to a chair at his side. "I want to ask you to do a little favor for me."

"Gladly, Father Prior!" exclaimed the young novice. "Whatever you wish!"

Prior Gonzalez leaned back in his chair and toyed with a long quill. He seemed to be enjoying some secret joke.

"Early tomorrow morning," he said, "we are expecting the arrival of six new brothers. I wondered how you would like to take the place of Father Guest Master for once, and receive them?"

"Oh, I should love that!" declared Fernando, smiling widely. "At what hour, Father Prior?"

"They will arrive about six o'clock, in time for breakfast. If you will welcome them and show each one to his cell, I will appreciate it greatly."

"I shall be most happy," said Fernando. Then he added, "I hope that Father Guest Master is not ill?"

Prior Gonzalez threw back his head and laughed.

"Father Matteo? There's no healthier monk in the whole monastery! He gets so much good exercise, trotting back and forth, and seeing to the needs of his guests, that he couldn't get sick if he tried."

Fernando hesitated a moment.

"I was wondering if," he said shyly, "if . . ."

"If what?" smiled the prior.

"Well, if perhaps you would like me to help him later at the hour when he feeds the poor?"

Prior Gonzalez shook his head.

"I know that is a duty you would love to perform, Fernando," he said kindly, "but you must wait a little. Wait until you, yourself, are wearing the white robe of an Augustinian monk. It won't be too long now," he added cheerfully. "The novice master has much good to say of your progress, and all your teachers are satisfied with your studies—especially your professor of rhetoric."

Fernando flushed happily.

"Thank you, Father Prior! I shall try all the harder now."

His heart was singing happily as he returned to the garden and picked up his hoe. Father Prior had honored him by asking a special service of him. He would be prompt at the front gate tomorrow to welcome the new brothers, and he would try to think of everything to make them feel at home. He must not forget to say a word to Brother Cook so that there would be a good breakfast waiting for them.

He had another hour of work in the garden before going to chapel and then to the study hall. As he dug around the cabbages, his mind went back over the events that had brought him here. He remembered as though it were yesterday his first visit to Father Prior on the morning after his vigil in the cathedral. He had hoped to be admitted to the monastery that very day! How disappointed he had been when Prior Gonzalez had said:

"You must wait until you are fifteen, Fernando."

"But, Father Prior, that's a long six months away!" he had protested.

"The time of waiting will give you an opportunity to learn more surely if this is really what God wants of you."

"But I know surely now!"

Prior Gonzalez had only shaken his head.

"This you owe to your parents," he had said. "You have not even spoken to them yet. You must do so at once. And you must win their consent. From what I know of your father, I do not think it will be easy."

"My mother, at least, will be pleased," Fernando had pointed out, "and although my father may try to prevent me, she will make him see that this is right."

"You must be very considerate of your father, for, after all, he has counted on you to take his place, and this will be a blow to him. You must also pray much. Come to visit me again when you are fifteen, and then we shall see. I can make no promises now."

He wasn't very encouraging, Fernando had thought as he walked slowly home. But that very night he found courage to speak to his parents. He would never forget the smile that had flashed across his mother's face. His father, however, had fallen into a towering rage. He would not hear of such a thing! The idea that his son, a de Bulhom, and heir to a vast fortune, should enter a monastery! It was absurd. He would knock such nonsense out of the boy's head. Fernando had been very unhappy when he went to bed.

But next day, after the fencing lesson in the armory, he told Sir Juan of his plan, while greatly fearing the knight's disappointment that he had given up the idea of becoming a squire. Sir Juan had opened his eyes wide in surprise, and then, with a broad grin, had thumped him heartily on the back.

"Fine, fine, young fellow!" he had cried. "We have always needed a monk in the family, and if this is what you want to do, I will stand right behind you, no matter what your father says!" Then he had given Fernando one of his searching looks. "I would not be surprised," he added teasingly, "if it was what I told you about the good monks following the crusades that has helped you to make up your mind!"

Fernando had flushed and stammered:

"Well, I cannot deny that I haven't thought about it," he admitted. Sir Juan was *something!* He knew everything that was in a boy's mind.

What was wonderful, and what Fernando even now did not understand, had been the sudden change in his father. He had expected to face a very difficult six months with Don Martinho. But the day following that first terrible interview, he had been surprised to see Canon Rodriguez coming out of his father's office. The canon, busy with his affairs at the cathedral, came very seldom to Castle de Bulhom. At dinner that night his father had leaned across the table and placed Fernando's dagger at his plate.

"Your uncle found this in the cathedral," he said briefly. "He thinks it belongs to you."

"Oh, thank you!" exclaimed Fernando, blushing. "I had forgotten . . ."

So the canon must have told his father about the vigil, and perhaps that had been why Don Martinho had raised no more objections. But what Fernando was never to know was that the canon had also told his father and mother about the cross in the stone.

Surprisingly, during his last six months at home, everything there at the castle had been very happy. To be sure, his friends pestered him with their constant invitations, refusing to understand why he no longer cared to accept these.

There had been only one great sadness. That was the day when Pedro had rushed up to him at school and, with tears streaming down his face, had told him that Sancho, his twin, had been drowned. Poor young Sancho had gone out in a boat with a fisherman. A violent storm had arisen, the boat had overturned, and both had been drowned. Fernando, his arms about Pedro, had felt his own heart breaking with sympathy for his friend. When at last he left home for the monastery, his parting gift to Sir Juan had been his beloved dagger which, ever after, the knight was to wear in his belt.

During the first six months at the monastery, none of the novices had been permitted to receive any visitors. But now for the past few weeks they had been allowed to see their families and friends two or three times a week. It was always wonderful when Don Martinho and Doña Tereza came. There was so much to tell, so much to hear!

And he loved to see Sir Juan riding through the monastery gates. The knight always rode Panzo and had Jingo running at his heels. After Jingo had jumped all over Fernando, and had soiled his black robe with his big paws, they would tie Panzo to a tree in the garden. Brother Cook would always find a sugar cake for the horse and a bone for Jingo. After Jingo had finished with it, and while Sir Juan and Fernando sat talking, he would tear around the garden, sniffing for a rabbit. Although he never found one, Jingo never gave up hope.

Yes, it had been wonderful to see his parents and Sir Juan; but Fernando was beginning almost to wish that his friends would not come. At first he had been glad to see them. Jaime had ridden over from Castle Almada with news that Isabella had been married to a young nobleman.

"Inez sent you a message," he said, "to say that she is delighted that you have entered the monastery and please not to forget your promise—whatever *that* may be!"

"Tell her that I shall not forget," smiled Fernando.

After that first visit Jaime always brought a group of friends with him. But the boys talked about things which no longer interested Fernando, and the girls all talked and giggled at once and tired him out. After the young people had left, he found it hard to settle down again to his studies and his prayers. He could not deny that sometimes he was homesick for the old life at the castle, and would give anything for a good talk with Pedro, his old schoolfriend. Now, as he bent busily over the cabbages, he was still thinking of these things when he heard the deep tones of the monastery bell calling him to chapel.

The next morning Fernando was up with the sun and waiting just inside the closed gates for the arrival of the six new brothers. It was such a pleasure to act for once as guest master! He hoped to give them a warm welcome—these young men who were so generously leaving the world to labor for God in the monastery. He wondered whether there would be any youths from Lisbon among them, or whether they came from faraway places, as did many who knocked at the gates of San Vicente. Just then he heard a loud rap, and with a merry smile he flung the gates wide.

"Welcome to San Vicente!" he cried and then stopped short as though the breath had been knocked from him. For there, grinning at him with his wide smile and from under his shock of red hair, stood Pedro. Fernando could scarcely believe his eyes. In a moment the two were hugging each other.

"I asked Father Prior to let me surprise you," explained Pedro.

"Well, you certainly did!" cried Fernando, leaning against the gate for support.

Later that day, at the recreation hour, they had a chance to talk. Pedro told him simply, "After we lost Sancho I began to see things differently. I no longer wanted a life of adventure but rather only to serve God. And I thought that, after Sancho, you were my best friend. So what better place to serve Him than where you are serving Him also?"

Fernando's face lit with pleasure. He said a prayer of thanksgiving in his heart for God's kindness in sending this old friend to the monastery. Their work would lie along different paths since Fernando was destined for the priesthood and Pedro for a humbler service. But at least they could see something of each other and talk over the boyhood memories they shared.

About two weeks later, at the hour for visitors, Fernando happened to glance out of a window to see Sir Juan riding into the courtyard. He looked handsomer than ever in a new doublet of black and silver, and he seemed to sit even straighter in the saddle. Fernando hastened down to meet him. As the knight swung a leg off Panzo's back he said:

"I have news for you, young fellow!"

Fernando couldn't imagine what it was, but anyway, it must be good, for Sir Juan looked very pleased with himself. When they reached the garden, the knight drew his sword and saluted Fernando.

"I have the honor of telling you that his majesty, the king, has just appointed your father, Don Martinho de Bulhom, the governor of all Lisbon!"

Fernando sat down quickly. This was a surprise— and a great honor for his father. For while he had been chief magistrate of Lisbon ever since Fernando could remember, and it was a position of importance, the post of governor was of far greater importance. After the king himself, it made his father absolute ruler over Lisbon and the wide territory about it. He listened as Sir Juan explained that the king had been so pleased with Don Martinho's service as chief magistrate that he had said that in all his kingdom of Portugal he could find no one more fitted to govern Lisbon than Don Martinho.

"The king is right!" cried Fernando happily. "But my father owes much to you, Sir Juan."

"Tush," said the knight, giving him a playful dig in the ribs. "It's all been fun. But now we are really going to be busy! Think of the people who will come running to your father for favors! I'll have to receive them all and try to keep them from bothering him. Think of the long, dull, state dinners that I'll have to sit through when I'd much rather be down at the port quelling a riot and knocking those scoundrels over the skull!"

They both fell to laughing as Sir Juan strode about, mimicking the manners of the court, for which he had never had much use anyway. Jingo barked and jumped about the knight's long legs and seemed to be laughing with them. Fernando was happy because he knew that his mother would be greatly pleased with all this. In her mind no honor was too great for Don Martinho.

Of all his studies in the monastery, the young novice liked best his classes in rhetoric. It had been hard, at first, to stand before others and try to deliver a sermon—almost as hard as it had been to speak before his class at school. Yet his heart was burning with the things he wanted to tell people about the love of God. If only he could overcome his shyness! Then he thought about Inez's Friend and began to pray to the Christ Child for help. In no time at all his shyness had vanished. Now he listened eagerly to the fine sermons of the older white-robed monks, learning from them and studying to improve his speech.

But whenever he sat down to write a sermon, sure as fate Father Guest Master would come knocking at his door to say that some friends were waiting for him in the parlor. Now that his father had been appointed governor of Lisbon, these were visiting the monastery even more frequently.

They were not only his gay young friends whom he had met at Castle Almada, but others from his early schooldays, and also many strangers whom he had never seen before. Almost all of them wanted to receive some favor from his father. It might be only a license to sell goods in the market place, or it might be some high position in the council of Lisbon. At first Fernando had been glad to help, sending them along with a letter to Sir Juan.

But gradually the news spread abroad that the governor of Lisbon could refuse his son nothing, and that if you wanted anything, the surest way to get it was to appeal to the young novice at San Vicente. Soon Fernando was so deluged with visitors that he could get little time for his work and prayers. Yet he wanted to help all of them and found it hard ever to say "no."

His cell was a tiny room, up a winding stone staircase at the top of the building. It had one small window that looked down upon the cloister garden. This was not the garden at the rear, where the vegetables grew and through which the poor passed every day to receive their bread. It was a small plot around which the monastery was built and was open to the sky. Here grass and bright-colored flowers grew. All the way around it there ran a narrow porch, supported by carved stone pillars. This was where the monks, the novices, and the brothers walked daily to chant their prayers together. They did this even on rainy days, for the porch was covered. It was called the cloister. During the summer Fernando loved to crane his neck out of the little window of his cell and look down upon the green grass and the bright, gay flowers growing in the cloister garden.

One morning after early Mass and breakfast, Fernando remembered that he had forgotten to bring a book from his cell which he would need in class. There was just time to run up and get it. Lifting his long robe, he took the stairs two at a time. When he reached his cell, to his surprise he saw that Pedro was there, on his hands and knees with a brush and a bucket of water, scrubbing the floor.

"Why, Pedro!" he exclaimed, astonished.

The other looked up with a happy grin.

"Didn't you know that I have been cleaning all the cells for the past week?"

"That explains why mine has never before been so clean!" said Fernando, reaching for his book. "Thank you very much, Pedro!"

Pedro leaned back on his heels. "I've been helping Brother Cook in the kitchen, too, and he tells me that he will yet make me the top cook in the monastery!" He threw back his red head in a roar of laughter. Fernando joined him.

"Heaven forbid!" he choked. "I don't want to be poisoned before I'm ordained!"

"Father Prior said that soon I will have to work only in the kitchen," Pedro added proudly, "but he has given me permission to continue to clean your cell."

"That's very kind of you and Father Prior," said Fernando, dashing for the stairs, "but you should

not be working for me. It is I who should be cleaning
your cell, and one day you'll be surprised to find me
doing it!"

Thus a year slipped by, and Fernando's seven-
teenth birthday was fast approaching. On that day
in August of 1212, it would be two years since he
had entered San Vicente. There had been but one
thing to mar his happiness—the constantly increas-
ing stream of visitors. He prayed to the Christ Child
for patience. Once, greatly troubled, he had gone to
Father Prior about it.

"It's this way, Fernando," Prior Gonzalez had
said gently. "In all charity, and following the way
of Christ, we cannot refuse to receive those who
come to us for help."

Fernando knew that he was right.

At the recreation hour there was always much
talk among the monks about the great monastery of
Santa Cruz, which lay many miles away in Coimbra,
the capital of Portugal. It also belonged to the Canons of St. Augustine and, in fact, it was called their
mother house because it was the first of their monas-
teries to be established in Portugal. It was said that
famous scholars taught there—men who had studied
at the great Universities of Paris and Bologna.
Fernando hoped that one day he would be able to
visit it.

Just before his birthday Sir Juan rode over one
day, looking more serious than usual.

"See here, young fellow," he said when they

were alone in the garden, "you've got to stop sending all these people to see your father. They're all
looking for jobs, and there are not enough jobs to
go around. They demand to see him, claiming they
are friends of yours. When they say that, Don
Martinho will never have them turned away. But
they waste his time, and they tire him out, and we
must remember . . ." He stopped, sighing a little.

"We must remember," Fernando added softly,
"that my father is growing older."

"Yes," said Sir Juan, looking into the serious
young eyes.

That night Fernando prayed long and earnestly
to the Christ Child. He did not know what to do to
avoid the visitors, but he felt sure that the Christ
Child would help him. It was at Mass the next morning when the answer came. Directly after breakfast he was knocking at the prior's door.

"Father Prior," he said, "can you have me trans-
ferred to the monastery of Santa Cruz at Coimbra?
It is far from Lisbon, and if I were there, no one
would pester me, seeking favors from my father!"

Prior Gonzalez understood. He, too, had reached
the point where he felt that something must be done
about Fernando's visitors. He put his hand upon the
youth's shoulder.

"We shall miss you," he said, "and at first you will
be lonely for your companions of San Vicente. But
after all, you will always be one of our family!"

On a day in September, Fernando set out for

Coimbra. He had decided to slip away from the monastery early in the morning to avoid the farewells which he knew would be painful. He had just begun to realize how much he would miss his good friends of San Vicente. As he hurried through the cloister with his small bundle of belongings under his arm, he suddenly heard the sound of running feet behind him. Turning, he saw Pedro rushing toward him with his usual wide grin, his red hair tousled and standing on end.

"Wait for me!" he called. "I'm going to Coimbra, too! They need a new cook at Santa Cruz, and Father Prior is sending me!"

Chapter Seven

CALL OF THE CRUSADES

On Christmas Day of the year 1216, four years after he had entered Santa Cruz, Fernando stood in the great carved pulpit of the ancient cathedral of Coimbra and looked out upon a thousand faces. He had preached here before; yet, for the trembling of his knees, each new time was just as hard as the last. He was glad that he could rest his hands upon the pulpit rail to steady himself and that the congregation could not see his shaking knees. But, as always, he bowed his head in silent prayer to the Child Jesus and, as always, the trembling ceased.

Almost everyone in Coimbra was here today, from king to serf, with the bishop himself seated to the left of the high altar. They had come to hear Fernando preach in the old cathedral. It had been erected after the crusaders had driven the Moors from Coimbra, now almost two centuries ago, and was built upon the ruins of a Moorish mosque.

Fernando had chosen for his text, "For God so loved the world as to give His only begotten Son. . . ." And it was on the love of God for man, and on the love of the Child Jesus for all, that Fernando spoke that Christmas morning.

The people, crowded closely together to the very doors, were hushed as the warm voice of the young Canon of St. Augustine rang out through the vast church. No one moved. No sound among them was heard except the occasional deep sighs which arose from many hearts.

When Mass was finished, Fernando was the first of the priests who had served at the altar to slip out through the sacristy door at the rear. He dreaded the compliments upon his sermon from clergy and people, which were sure to follow if he lingered. Besides, he was in a great hurry to get back to the monastery where he had an important appointment.

As he hastened alone along the path that led to Santa Cruz, the square before the cathedral was filling up with the people who were pouring out of the great doors. Noblemen and knights, lords and their ladies, tradesmen and serfs stood respectfully to one side as the king and queen with their attendants passed. The king, who was built on roly-poly lines, was Alphonso II, but behind his back everyone called him "Alphonso, the Fat." Yet they liked him because he was a brave warrior and because his queen was very religious.

Now the square rang with cheery Christmas greetings as one called out to another, and the ladies stopped to chat with their friends. Everyone was talking about the sermon they had just heard.

"He becomes greater every time he preaches!" declared Doña Maria of the noble house of Carrero. "And he is still so young! I hear that he was only ordained in August. He can't be more than twenty-one."

"Well, he has studied under great masters at Santa Cruz," replied her friend. "Where else in all Portugal could he have found such scholars as those who have come to the monastery from the University of Paris?"

"True, and it is said that he is the most brilliant of all their students," nodded Doña Maria. "I remember him when he was a little boy at the Castle de Bulhom which we often visited. He was forever followed about by a big spotted hound. The two were inseparable," she laughed. "Who would then have dreamed that such a lively boy would grow up to throw away a great fortune and become a monk?"

"With his father as governor, I cannot imagine why he ever left Lisbon for Coimbra!" exclaimed the other.

And so the talk ran while Fernando, quite unconscious of it all, hastened onward to meet his poor. The monastery of Santa Cruz lay at the edge of the city.

During the summer, on that great day when he had been ordained a priest, he had received the post in the monastery for which he had seriously prayed. He had been appointed Father Guest Master of Santa Cruz. This he had wanted that he might daily serve the poor. He must also welcome other guests, mainly the rich nobles who brought gifts and money to Santa Cruz which helped him to buy food for his poor. He especially enjoyed the visits of the knights who came, full of talk of the warfare against the Moors. Fernando never tired of listening to them.

When he arrived at the monastery, he hurried down through the long corridors to the big kitchen at the rear where Pedro was now installed as Brother Cook. The door which opened into the hall was divided into two halves—that is, the upper half could be opened for air and the lower half could remain closed. As he approached, Fernando saw that only the upper half was open. He could see Pedro's red head, but not the rest of him, for the cook was seated on a low bench. Fernando was amazed to see that great tears were coursing down the usually merry face. Some dreadful misfortune must have befallen his friend! Fernando's heart stood still.

"My poor Pedro!" he cried anxiously. "What is the trouble?"

"Onions," replied Pedro briefly, not lifting his head.

Fernando pushed open the door's lower half. Then he and Brother Luis, who was Pedro's helper, laughed until they ached at the sight of Brother Cook weeping into the large bowl of onions he was peeling.

"I'll tell you what," said Pedro, looking up and grinning through his tears, "you may have all the rest of the onions for your poor!" He pointed to a large sack standing nearby, the gift of a rich friend. "Let *them* do the peeling, and welcome!"

"It's a bargain!" cried Fernando, hauling the sack to the door at the rear which opened onto the garden. "And what else have you saved for my friends today?" he asked, peering into all the pots and kettles. "There are fifty loaves of bread over there," said Pedro, nodding toward a shelf. "There is also some splendid cold meat, left over from last night, although not enough for all. You'll have to hold back on it and give it to the hungriest."

"Thank you, Brother Cook," smiled Fernando gaily as he began to sort out the food on a table which stood near the outer door. Flinging it open, he saw a long line of his friends approaching. Each carried a basket, and the children stood back to let the old people go first. Fernando knew each face and, as they came up, he had a smile and a word for everyone.

"How is your father today, Menendez? Better? That's good! Give him this meat; it will put strength into him!" And, "I'm sorry that your back pains you again, Maria. Here is a jar of ointment I've been saving for you. Rub it in well. I'm sure it will help."

The visitors cried out their thanks as they moved away with baskets filled to overflowing, and more than one knelt to ask a blessing from the white-robed monk. Now only a small boy lingered.

"What is it, Carlos?" asked Fernando, bending down to the sad little face.

The child fought to keep back the tears from his big eyes.

"It's my father," he whispered. "He's been away from home now for many months, and my mother and I do not know where to find him."

"Oh, that's too bad," said Fernando, drawing the boy down beside him on a bench. He put his arm around Carlos and said:

"Tell me all about it."

Pedro and Brother Luis were busy with their pots and pans and paid no attention.

"My mother weeps all the time," confided Carlos. "And I—I—oh, I miss my father very much!" He buried his face against the monk's shoulder.

Fernando stroked the small dark head.

"One can be very lonely for one's father," he agreed. "But I have a plan that will help you. But first let me tell you a story."

"Oh, please do!" said the child, looking up at him.

"Once long ago there was a little Boy Who was separated from His Father. He missed Him greatly. The Boy was the Son of God. He went on a journey with His mother and His foster father. In the city they visited there was a large church which was called the Temple. But the Boy always called it His Father's house. When the visit was over and they started home again, the Boy ran away. For three long days His mother and foster father searched for Him. At last they found Him in His Father's house, where He had gone because He was so lonely for His Father, and where He could feel close to Him, and could also do something that would please Him."

"The Child Jesus!" exclaimed Carlos, sitting up with a smile.

Fernando nodded. "Now Carlos, since the Child Jesus once so greatly missed His Father, He will understand exactly how you feel. He will be your Friend and help you if you ask Him."

"Oh, I *will* ask Him!" cried Carlos, slipping off the bench and picking up his basket. "Thank you very much, Canon Fernando!" And off he trotted, smiling happily.

Later on that Christmas Day Fernando was summoned to the prior's office. As he entered, Prior

Vincent looked up at him out of his steady gray eyes.

"You preached well today, Fernando, and were a credit to Santa Cruz. I'm sure that your words cured many a soul that had long been sick."

"Thank you, Father Prior," said Fernando simply.

"It would seem as though God were rewarding you for that sermon," continued the older monk, "for I have just received news that during the New Year season your parents will be visiting Coimbra as guests of the king. They hope to see much of you!"

Fernando was happily surprised. He had not seen his parents for some time, although during his four years at Santa Cruz he had been more fortunate in this respect than others, since Don Martinho was frequently called to Coimbra on business for the king. Sometimes he sent Sir Juan, and these brief meetings with those he loved had been happy interludes in his strict routine. Now he wished that Sir Juan were coming also, but his father and the knight could hardly be absent from Castle de Bulhom at the same time.

"I hope that your parents will dine often at the monastery," continued Prior Vincent kindly. "Your father, the governor, would honor us."

As Fernando thanked him and went on his way to the chapel, Prior Vincent reflected that it had been a lucky day for Santa Cruz when young de

Bulhom had knocked at the gates. At that time he had never dreamed that the slender youth of seventeen would, at twenty-one, become the greatest preacher in a community that was famous for its preaching the country over.

When his mother and father arrived in the city a few days later, Doña Tereza was very happy to hear of Fernando's skill in the pulpit. The queen herself had said to her, "Doña Tereza, your son has a golden tongue!"

But upon the first visit to the monastery his mother regarded him anxiously.

"Son, you look tired and pale. You must not over-work, even in so great a cause!"

Fernando only laughed and said teasingly, "Keep an eye on that husband of yours! He looks tired and pale, too."

Don Martinho slapped him on the shoulder and cried, "Nonsense! I never felt better in my life!"

While the delighted Pedro took Doña Tereza off to show her his big kitchen, Don Martinho sat down for a talk with his son.

"Again we are harassed by the Moors," he said. "They are making raids in certain areas. It is likely that soon we shall have to launch a crusade against them."

Fernando's eyes lit up.

"You will go yourself, Father?"

"Yes, at the king's command. Also Sir Juan and

the others from the castle. King Alphonso will lead the crusade."

Fernando clutched the edge of the bench until his nails went white. It was all he could do not to cry out, "I'm coming, too!" But he had pledged his obedience to the monastery, and he knew that, unless Prior Vincent were to release him, he could not move from Santa Cruz.

Not many months later, in 1217, Don Martinho and Sir Juan rode off in King Alphonso's army. They met the Moors at Alcácer do Sol and won a great victory. Those months of waiting had been very hard on Fernando in the monastery. He was restless, and at night his sleep was sorely troubled. Constantly he dreamed that he was back again in the armory of Castle de Bulhom, selecting the weapon he would use in battle against the Moors. He was glad when the warfare was ended.

One summer day about two years later, at the hour when the poor were expected, he was standing at his usual post in the kitchen beside a table laden with food. As he watched his friends approach, he called out suddenly, "Pedro! Come here a moment!"

Pedro dropped the big spoon with which he was stirring a pot over the fire and hurried to the door.

"Look there," said Fernando, "at the end of that line—those two strangers. Have you ever seen them before?"

Pedro shook his head and exclaimed, "Why,

they look just like monks in those long robes! Only —only they seem different, somehow."

The two strangers hung back until all the baskets had been filled. Then they came forward, smiling.

"We are beggars also, Canon Fernando," one said. "Through the sweet charity of Christ, may we have a bit of bread?"

Fernando looked at their poor robes, which were woven of rough gray wool such as only the serfs wore, and at their bare feet. He stretched out his hands in welcome.

"Bread and meat you shall have, my friends!" he exclaimed with a smile. "But come inside and tell us about yourselves, for I can see that you are strangers to this country."

He flung the door wide, and Pedro drew up another bench.

The tall, thin one with the long, slender face introduced himself.

"I am Friar Raphael," he said. Then, turning toward his companion, who was short and stout, he continued, "And this is Friar Giorgio. We are Friars Minor from Italy."

Both smiled widely from sunburned faces, showing their white, even teeth.

"I would know you at once for sons of Italy," exclaimed Fernando, "for Italy's sun seems to be reflected in your smiles! Sit down, sit down! Pedro, please bring our guests something to eat."

"Although you do not know us," said Raphael as

they settled themselves, "we know you. We have often heard you preach in the cathedral."

"How is that, if you are strangers to Coimbra?" asked Fernando.

"We have been here for some months," explained Giorgio. "But our little friary lies in the country at some distance from the city. And, as yet, very few people know that it is there."

"The queen herself gave it to us," went on Raphael. "That is, she gave it to our Father Francis when she learned that he needed a house in Portugal where our missionaries could stop when on their way to Morocco."

Fernando was becoming more and more puzzled. He had never heard of this friary.

"Morocco?" he asked. "You are missionaries, then?"

"Oh, yes!" declared Giorgio. "We are missionaries to the poor everywhere—here, there, in Italy, and all over." He waved his short arm widely. "We now desire to send missionaries to Morocco to convert the Moors, for when that is done, there will be no more warfare between them and Christian people."

"Father Francis himself hopes to join a crusade to the Holy Land that he may convert the Saracens," went on Raphael as Pedro put plates of steaming food before them. "When he was a youth, he wanted with all his heart to be a crusader."

Something stirred within Fernando.

"Tell me all about your Father Francis," he said.

The two friars looked at each other for a moment and then burst into merry laughter.

"Were we to start, we should never finish," cried Raphael, "for there is no one in the world like him!"

"Where does he live?" pressed Fernando.

"In the Italian hills in a town called Assisi. He was born there, and there he founded the Order of Friars Minor. But most of the time he lives by the roadside, and in the forests, and in caves, as he walks through the country preaching to the poor and through the great cities preaching to the rich."

"But why are you called Friars Minor?" asked Fernando.

"Because in Italy the poorest people are known as the *Minores*," explained Giorgio. "And Father Francis so loves the poor that he wanted to create an order which would serve them above all. And he knew that one cannot truly serve the poor unless one becomes as poor as the poorest—just as poor as our Lord was when He was upon earth. Father Francis strives to imitate our Lord in all that he does."

"He gave up a great fortune to do all this," went on Raphael, "for his father was one of the richest men in all that country!"

Pedro said excitedly, "But many holy men do that to follow God! Here is Canon Fernando . . ."

Fernando stopped him with a warning glance and then asked:

"How, then, do you live if you are all so poor?"

"We work with our hands in the fields, or at whatever trade we know, to earn our bread for the day. When we cannot find work, we beg our daily bread in the Name of Christ. That is why we came to your door today," said Giorgio simply. "Our friars have been preaching every day in the market place, and they are hungry."

Fernando arose and began heaping fruits and vegetables into a big sack. But Friar Raphael jumped up and held his arm.

"Not so much, dear Canon Fernando, not so much! You have a great heart! But Father Francis wants us to accept only what we need for the day."

"Then you will come again another day?" asked Fernando eagerly. "I wish very much to hear more of your Father Francis!"

"Oh, yes!" exclaimed the two. Then Giorgio added, "We will come if only to ask your blessing, for we have heard you preach."

Fernando felt greatly embarrassed. Beside these two happy beggars he felt poor and cheap. He looked down at his white robe of finely woven wool and at his good sandals. Then he looked again at the coarse garb of the friars and marveled how, with the little they had and the hard life they led, they could seem so incredibly happy.

"Father Francis is full of joy," said Raphael, "and

he loves to sing with his friars. Would you like us to sing some of the praises of God he has composed?"

"Gladly!" exclaimed Fernando.

So Friar Raphael and Friar Giorgio raised their heads and let their warm Italian voices ring out. Pedro and Fernando were delighted.

"Now here is a merry tune he invented," said Giorgio, "and you must both listen and then join us in the chorus!"

It was a gay, rollicking melody, and soon Fernando and Pedro were singing along lustily with them. They were having a wonderful time when suddenly Father Prior's head appeared through the half-open door. The singing stopped abruptly. Father Prior looked so amazed that Pedro had all he could do to stifle his laughter.

"Your pardon, Father Prior!" exclaimed Fernando quickly. "Our guests here were teaching us a song of Italy."

Prior Vincent smiled thinly.

"I only feared you were disturbing those who are at prayer," he said. "We could hear you all over the monastery!"

When he had left, the two friars expressed their sorrow for having embarrassed Fernando.

"We forgot ourselves," said Giorgio. "You and Pedro were so kind that we thought we were back in our own little friary!"

"Come again soon!" cried Fernando, as they

parted with laughter and many thanks for the sack
of food. "And when you do, be sure to bring those
missionaries to Morocco with you!" he called after
them.

Chapter Eight

Martyrs of Morocco

When, in the summer of 1219, Fernando had first met the Friars Minor, there was hardly a person in all Coimbra, save the queen, who knew them. But now, on a lovely spring day of the year 1220, the entire city had turned out to honor them.

The streets were thronged with people, all moving toward the cathedral, and many were there from far cities who had come, at the king's request, to the great ceremony of welcome. Knights on their horses charged over the roads; great ladies passed in their coaches; and the poor moved in a never-ending stream.

It was a strange ceremony of welcome to which the king had invited them, for the welcome was offered to no living person. Before the high altar of the ancient cathedral there rested five coffins of the holy dead. They held the remains of the five great Franciscan martyrs of Morocco. It was to these five hitherto-unknown Friars Minor that, on that day, all Portugal was paying homage.

Prince Pedro himself, the king's brother, had escorted their bodies with all honor from Morocco to Coimbra.

Fernando, with his brothers from Santa Cruz, knelt within the cathedral sanctuary as the solemn Mass of thanksgiving progressed. The multitude filled every corner and spread out through the open doors into the square beyond. The king and the queen and Prince Pedro were there, and the bishop himself was preaching the sermon.

As the bishop's voice rang out in praise of the five Friars Minor, Fernando was thinking of his good fortune in having known them a little. Just before their departure for Morocco, Friar Raphael had brought the missionaries to the monastery. They had talked long about their Father Francis and of his plan for them to convert the infidel with the cross and their preaching. They were to fight a crusade with no other weapon than the cross. When they had walked away down the garden path of Santa Cruz, they had turned several times to wave merrily to Fernando, who stood at the door, feeling that these happy men were taking his heart with them. The heart came from a long line of crusaders.

Now, from the pulpit, he heard the bishop's voice name the five—Bernard, Pietro, Adjutua, Accurso, and Otho. While the great crowd listened in tense silence, the bishop explained the manner of their deaths. They had left Coimbra last summer, sailing from Lisbon for Morocco. They had boldly carried the cross and their preaching into the heart of the infidel country. The prince of Morocco, alarmed at their success, had feared that all his people would go over to Christianity, so he had ordered that all five missionaries should be brutally slain.

They had died bravely together, these five Friars Minor, at the point of a Saracen sword. The bishop declared that as they died, each had proclaimed loudly that Jesus Christ was God, Son of God. They had died as true crusaders—with one difference, which made them even greater heroes. Save for the cross of Christ which they carried, they had been unarmed. These men had been followers of Francis, the Little Poor Man of Assisi, as he was called.

Great wonders had accompanied their deaths. The sick had been miraculously healed, and many of the people had been converted.

"His royal highness, our great Prince Pedro himself, was saved through their intercession for him in heaven," concluded the bishop.

When the ceremony was over, Fernando, with the canons of Santa Cruz and the Friars Minor from the little friary beyond the city, followed with bent heads the procession which formed behind the five caskets. These were being carried in state from the cathedral to rest beneath the chapel floor of Santa Cruz. For this thing Prior Vincent had requested— that his monastery might have the honor of being the final resting place of the glorious martyrs of Morocco. After the canons and the friars there followed a long line of the faithful, anxious to make their prayers at the tomb of the holy five.

The chapel was too small to hold them all, and they overflowed into the courtyard and down the road. Fernando, with the canons and the Friars Minor, knelt near the tomb. As the day wore on, and the chanting died away, and one by one the candles flickered out, there were, at last, only Fernando and a few others who lingered.

As he knelt there, Fernando was thinking about these strange Friars Minor. They had buried all pride. They did not mind being beggars. How could a rich man's son ever bring himself to beg? Yet Francis had been a rich man's son. . . . And their poor garments! How could a rich man's son tolerate the coarse, ill-shaped robes they wore next to their skins? Yet Francis had been a rich man's son.

Fernando remembered that on the day of his

meeting with the missionaries he had questioned their leader, Friar Bernard:

"Is your Father Francis a priest?"

"Oh, no," the other had answered. "He always says that he is not worthy of being a priest. He says that he leaves that to those who are more holy than he."

"But surely very few are as holy as he?" ventured Fernando.

"True," replied Bernard as he bowed his head reverently. "There is no one who is as holy as our Father Francis. Yet he thinks nothing of himself."

Kneeling there, reflecting on all these things, other thoughts, too, came rushing into Fernando's mind to interrupt his prayers. He tried to banish them but could not. He had to let them run their course. A picture of Sir Juan and himself arose in his mind on a day when they were seated in the monastery garden shortly after the missionaries had left for Morocco. Sir Juan had been in the capital on business for Don Martinho. The conversation came back to Fernando now. He had said to Sir Juan:

"Supposing—supposing that I should be called away from the monastery and should be gone for some time. Do you think that it would disturb my parents greatly?"

"Not if you were happy about what you were doing," replied Sir Juan, regarding him keenly.

"Well, supposing that I were gone a long time

and that if, during that time, anything should happen to my parents . . ." Fernando hesitated.

"Yes?" pressed Sir Juan.

"Supposing that should happen," he hurried on, "there are a few things that I should be grateful to you for doing for me."

"Of course," replied Sir Juan with a smile. "Anything!"

"Well, for one, would you see that many Masses were offered for their souls?"

"But of course!"

"And there's another thing," Fernando had added. "I often think of my dog, Jingo."

"Oh, he's fine!" declared the other, laughing. "Still smelling for rabbits and almost as frisky as when he was a puppy. And he's a regular pet with the cook."

Fernando had smiled at that. "Well," he said, "if anything were to happen to my parents, it might be best for Jingo to find a new home. And I was wondering if . . ." Again he hesitated.

Sir Juan poked him in the ribs. "Out with it, young fellow!" he said.

"Perhaps if you would be kind enough to take Jingo over to the Castle Almada, Inez might like to have him as a pet?"

"Wonderful idea! I saw the Lady Inez not long ago. She is quite grownup now and has a lovely face. She still walks on crutches, but I believe I never saw so happy a face."

"I think I know why that is," said Fernando quietly.

"She would be glad to have Jingo," continued Sir Juan, "and you may be sure that if any of these events should come to pass, I will safely deliver him to the Castle Almada." Then he added, regarding Fernando out of the corner of a twinkling eye, "You wouldn't be thinking of following the crusades, would you, young fellow?"

Sir Juan was terrible! Even now, at Fernando's age, the knight still could guess everything that was in a fellow's heart.

Kneeling there in the monastery chapel at the tomb of the martyrs, Fernando had to smile in spite of himself at the memory of that conversation.

Once again his thoughts reverted to Francis of Assisi who had inspired the five holy dead who lay there. He reflected that during the year while he, Fernando de Bulhom, had been wearing a fine white robe, and had been buried over his books and his study to become a priest, this Francis, feeling himself unworthy of the priesthood, was wearing the garment of the poor and begging his bread. His heart aflame with love for God and man, he had been out on the highways caring for the sick and washing the leper's sores. He had been consumed with a burning desire to follow the crusades and to die as a martyr for Christ, even as his five holy followers had done.

Fernando heard a slight stir at his side and turned

to see Friar Zacchary, the prior of the Friars Minor in Coimbra, now rising from his knees. Fernando stretched out a hand and caught at his long sleeve.

"Wait for me in the garden," he whispered. "I will be right there."

With a final prayer, he followed Zacchary into the garden. Friar Raphael was also there, and Friar Giorgio, and a half dozen others of the Friars Minor. Fernando walked quickly to Zacchary's side and turned to face the others.

"Most beloved brothers," he said smilingly, "with a rejoicing heart I would put on the gray garment of your order, but only on the condition—" he turned to their prior—"that you send me at once to the Saracen country that I may die as a martyr for Christ!"

They looked at him in astonishment, scarcely able to believe their ears—that the famous Canon Fernando, the most gifted preacher in all Portugal, should wish to join their humble order! It was incredible. After a long pause Friar Zacchary said gently:

"It would make us most happy to have you as one of us. But I question the wisdom of your decision. It has been made too quickly."

"I have been thinking of it for a long time!" eagerly protested Fernando.

"Nevertheless, such a serious step requires great consideration." Then, as Zacchary watched Fernando's face darken with disappointment, he added,

"All Coimbra expects to hear you preach at the cathedral during Lent. You should not disappoint the people, or your own Father Prior. Go through these six weeks with humility and preach well, and keep a prayer in your heart for the guidance of God. If, at the end of Lent, you should still feel as you do now, we will welcome you gladly as a Friar Minor!"

"And then will you send me at once to Morocco?" demanded Fernando.

"Ah, that I cannot promise. You must first live with us for a while at our little friary and learn the ways of a Friar Minor. They are hard ways, Fernando, ways of poverty and often of hunger. But they are also ways of joy. They are quite different from the ways you have followed here."

"I shall embrace them with happiness!" cried Fernando. "And I'm sure that it will not be long until you find me fit to go as a missionary to Morocco!"

So it was agreed that the final decision would be made right after Easter. With happy hearts they said farewell, and Fernando turned to walk back to the monastery through the garden. He was wondering how difficult it was going to be to win Prior Vincent's consent to abandon the white robe of the Canons of St. Augustine. As he walked, his head down, puzzling over the problem, he did not see the little figure awaiting him at the kitchen door. When a small hand reached out and caught his robe, he was startled. Looking down, he beheld young Carlos.

"I've been waiting for you," said the boy shyly. "I want to tell you something." The small face was all smiles.

"That's very nice of you, Carlos," said Fernando, smiling back at him. "And what is this great thing?"

"My father has returned! And I wanted to tell you how happy my mother and I are that he is home again!"

Fernando lifted the boy up and swung him through the air a couple of times. "That's wonderful!" he exclaimed heartily. Then, as he set him down again, he asked, "And how do you think this great thing has come to pass, Carlos?"

"Because I asked the Child Jesus to return him to us," said the boy simply.

"But of course!" cried Fernando. "Now come into the kitchen, and I'm sure that Brother Cook will give you a big basket of cookies to take home!"

Lent was over, and never before had Fernando preached so brilliantly. People had come from far and wide to hear him. After the Mass on Easter morning, he sought out Prior Vincent to ask for his release from Santa Cruz.

There followed a most difficult hour. Prior Vincent was angry and hurt by Fernando's decision. Could it be possible that his finest scholar and preacher should prefer the poor beggars of Assisi to the renowned Canons of St. Augustine? He argued long with the young man, but at length, with a sigh, he arose and said, "You cannot leave Santa Cruz unless you have the consent of the entire community. If you should win that, my hands will be tied. I can do nothing more to keep you here!"

It proved hard indeed to gain the consent of the entire community. Most of the canons had come to be very fond of Fernando, and they understood, too, how important his preaching was to the monastery. But, at last, after some time, he was able to persuade them. Prior Vincent was forced, with a heavy heart, to send word to Friar Zacchary to come and take away his new Friar Minor.

On a day in the early fall of 1220, Zacchary arrived with Friar Raphael and Friar Giorgio. Friar Raphael carried over his arm the new robe of coarse gray wool which they would slip over Fernando's head in the chapel. All the community of Santa Cruz was there to witness the ceremony. Fernando laid his fine white robe at the feet of Prior Vincent and bowed his head to receive the other. As he left the chapel with the three Friars Minor, many sighs went up from the canons, and some of the eyes were moist. Then, in the silence, a voice rang out, suddenly, bitterly:

"Go on, Fernando!" it cried. "Go on and become a Friar Minor! Go on and become a saint—for all *we* care!"

Fernando's step faltered. He had recognized the voice. It was that of his old professor in theology, the famous Master Matthew of Paris. But the sarcasm and bitterness in the voice did not make him angry. For all his humility, he recognized Master Matthew's grief at losing his favorite student in theology. He passed out of the chapel with bowed head and a prayer of affection in his heart for his old master.

It was strange. Never before had he felt, at one and the same time, as happy or as sad. He knew that he was going as God was directing him. At the same time he knew that he was leaving forever many whom he loved to embark on a strange life among strangers.

They had reached the courtyard and were walking toward the monastery gates when they heard the sound of running feet pounding behind them. Turning, they saw Pedro, his red hair standing on end as usual, and with a small bundle under his arm.

"Wait for me, Fernando!" he called breathlessly. "Father Prior has given me permission to go with you!"

Chapter Nine

ANTHONY OF THE OLIVE TREES

THE vessel lifted her saffron sails and flew like a great bird across the deep blue waters of the bay of Lisbon. They sparkled in the sunlight of a bright autumn day of the year 1220.

Fernando and Pedro stood at the prow, felt the salt spray on their faces, and were immensely happy. The captain and the sailors regarded the two curiously—the handsome young man with the great dark eyes set deeply under a wide brow and the smooth,

olive skin; and his companion with the merry face
and the red hair. The rough gray robe of the Friars
Minor looked odd to the seamen. They had not seen
it before. It had been another captain and another
crew which, many months before, had conveyed
the five martyrs to Morocco.

"Look," said Fernando, pointing toward shore
where a dark mass arose grimly against the white
beach. "Do you remember those rocks?"

"Shall I ever forget them!" laughed Pedro. "Or
the day we climbed up them to meet Old Lopez!"
After a moment he added seriously, "I think, Fernando, that from that day you began to change."

The other only smiled and looked down into the
blue water rushing past the prow as it cut into the
sea. He was reminded of the cross in the stone made
on that very day but of which he had never spoken
to anyone—not even to Pedro.

On their rushed journey from Coimbra to Lisbon
there had been little time for talk, so bent were they
upon an early arrival at the port that they might
sail on this particular vessel. After many months of
hesitation, the good Friar Zacchary had finally made
arrangements for their passage. The journey, rapid
though it was, had left them only an hour in Lisbon.

It was better so, thought Fernando. Above all he
did not wish to linger in his native city, for in that
case he would have felt drawn irresistibly to the
Castle de Bulhom. But there he could not go just
now, for his parents would be sure to use every

means in their power to prevent him from undertaking what they would have called his "mad crusade." Fernando knew quite well that they had no desire to see their son become another martyr of Morocco.

However, he had been glad that during the hour spent on the wharf watching the ship take on her cargo Pedro had been able to scurry up the beach for a brief visit with his own mother and father. Pedro returned in a mood not so happy as that in which he had set forth.

"My father has aged," he told Fernando with a sigh, "and does not seem well. He is no longer able to work at his trade of blacksmith. I worry for my mother. Should she lose him, she would be all alone in the world."

Fernando's eyes softened with sympathy. "We will pray for him," he said simply, "and trust the good God to take care of him."

With that Pedro had brightened and had busied himself examining everything on the wharf. Now and then he raised his head to sniff the air with a delighted grin. Mingled with the smell of the sea there were many unpleasant odors, thought Fernando; yet he could see that every sniff was like perfume to Pedro who had spent his boyhood at the port.

Now, as the two stood at the prow and the vessel made for the open sea, they talked much of the friary near Coimbra which they had left only a few days before. The Friars Minor had named it "Saint Anthony of the Olive Trees" because it was surrounded by a grove of such trees and was shaded by their cool, silvery leaves. Also, because a saint who was named Anthony had, nine long centuries before, been the first Christian monk. When Christianity was young he had lived a life of great holiness in the desert. The Friars Minor in Coimbra had chosen him as their patron.

"Never have I been in such a holy place as the friary," declared Pedro. "But I must confess that it was a rude shock when I first saw it that day there in the olive grove after our long walk from Santa Cruz."

"And to me, also," smiled Fernando. "After the great monastery where we had lived, it looked like nothing but a small shack. But oh, Pedro, what peace we found within the narrow limits of that little friary!"

"Peace, yes," agreed Pedro. "But I shall never forget the moment when they showed me what they called the kitchen! How could anyone call it a kitchen?" He doubled up with laughter. "Instead of a fireplace, they had an open pit in the ground for cooking. Instead of pots and pans, they had a couple of rusty old kettles. Rather than plates, we ate off pieces of tin—that is, when we ate at all!" Again he bent double with laughter.

"All very good for the health," smiled Fernando, "although I admit it must have been hard on you, accustomed to a fine kitchen, to find nothing to cook and nothing to cook it in!"

"Kitchen or no, the friars themselves were wonderful," said Pedro. "Never have I laughed so much, or been among so happy a lot. And the singing!"

"We shall miss the singing," agreed Fernando, "unless we encounter other friars in Morocco."

"Friar Zacchary said this would not be likely just now," remarked Pedro. "That was why he counseled you to wait a few months longer. He expects that Father Francis will send more missionaries out in the spring."

A shadow crossed the other's face. Clearly he remembered all his talks with Friar Zacchary during the past six months and how the older man had tried to persuade him to wait. But Fernando kept reminding him that it was on this condition that he had joined the Friars Minor—that he should be sent at once to preach to the Saracens and to die as a martyr for Christ.

"It is very hard to die *alone* as a martyr," Friar Zacchary had objected. "If you would only wait until our Father Francis sends out other missionaries! Last time there were five, you know, bound for Morocco. They could sustain and comfort each other. But if you go now, you will have only Pedro— and I doubt very much if Pedro wants to die as a martyr for Christ!"

That had set them both to laughing, but Fernando had assured Zacchary that, at the first sign of hostility from the Saracens, he would send Pedro straight back to Portugal. He had also made Pedro understand the same thing.

As it was, the two had remained six months at Saint Anthony of the Olive Trees, learning the simple ways of the Friars Minor. They had worked in the fields to earn their daily bread and had shared it with the poor; they had begged at the roadsides; they had cared for the sick and the dying; they had daily sung the praises of God. And Fernando had preached in the streets of Coimbra to the throngs who came to hear him. At last Friar Zacchary could hold out no longer against his persuasions and had to give the young man his way.

Fernando remembered all these things as the wind rose and drove the ship along. He gripped the rail and looked upward through the saffron sails into the white clouds chasing each other across a serene blue sky. His heart sang with happiness and thanksgiving. At last he was on his way to fulfill the dream which had possessed him ever since he could remember. When he was no more than seven, he had determined to become a crusader, to follow in the footsteps of his ancestors. Now, at the age of twenty-five, he was setting forth on his first crusade.

To be sure, it was somewhat different from those crusades he had dreamed of as a boy, back there in the armory of Castle de Bulhom. He touched the large crucifix which hung upon his breast. This was a better weapon than the bright blades over which he had lingered there in the old armory. He thought of Sir Juan and uttered a little sigh. He would miss him and the fighting he had once hoped to do at his side to recapture Jerusalem from the Saracens. But this was a better way to win for Christ.

His thoughts were interrupted as Pedro suddenly clutched his arm.

"Look! Out there!" he pointed.

Fernando turned to see, at some distance, a great black hulk of a ship etched against the sunset.

"It looks like the ship of Old Lopez!" exclaimed Pedro. "I believe it's the *San Diabolo* herself! Wouldn't it be fun if we should be set upon by pirates?"

"Not before we have converted the Moors!" exclaimed his companion.

At that moment the captain approached and said respectfully to Fernando, "Friar Anthony, your supper is waiting, if you and Brother Pedro would like to take it now."

As they turned to go below, Pedro whispered to Fernando, "I shall never, *never* get used to hearing you called Friar Anthony!"

"But Pedro, you must remember that Anthony is now my name. From now on you must try to call me Anthony and not Fernando."

"But I have called you Fernando ever since I can remember," protested Pedro, running a puzzled hand through his tousled red hair. "It's very hard to change now."

"I know," said the other. "It *is* hard. But this is the custom of the Friars Minor in Coimbra. The new friars always give up their old names and take new ones. The name Anthony was given me because the friary is dedicated to Saint Anthony, and because I greatly admire that holy man of the desert. So Friar Anthony I am from now on and always!"

"I shall try to remember," said Pedro meekly. "I'll do my best, Fernando—I mean, Anthony!" he quickly added.

Then they both laughed and sat down to an excellent supper.

It was a fair wind that blew them into Ceuta, the port of Morocco, although the night before had been stormy and rough at sea. The new Anthony had been so cold that he had risen from his bunk to walk the decks where, in spite of the storm, he felt warmer than in his cabin. He was still shivering when the big wharf came in view. The shore seemed to be lined with dark, eager faces, capped with white turbans, watching the ship come in. His heart lifted. Here were souls, souls whom he could win for Christ—thousands of souls! With the help of God he would win them by his preaching and by a martyr's death.

But the moment he set foot on shore a strange dizziness suddenly overcame him. He had to clutch at Pedro's arm to keep from falling.

"What is it?" asked his frightened friend, looking with alarm at the deeply flushed face.

"I don't know," mumbled Anthony. "But—but I think I must sit down somewhere."

Pedro found a bench and then ran off to find one of the sailors. He came back almost at once.

"He says there is a small inn only a few steps from here where the seamen stay when they are in port. He thinks that the landlord will rent us a room."

When Anthony tried to rise, his knees felt very wobbly, and the arm he placed through Pedro's was burning with fever. With great effort he reached the inn and sank upon the crude bed, none too clean, in the tiny room under the roof which had been given them. Pedro ran off to fetch a doctor.

The man was French, but he had lived so long under the hot sun of Morocco that his skin was as dark as the natives'.

"Your friend is very sick," he whispered to Pedro at the door after he had examined the friar, "and may have to remain in bed for many weeks. He has contracted the native fever which carries off many a traveler from Europe."

Poor Pedro looked very distressed. The doctor left some medicines, told him how to care for the patient, and promised to return next day. Anthony lay moaning and tossing on the bed, not knowing where he was. Sometimes he imagined that he was back in the old armory of Castle de Bulhom, fencing with Sir Juan.

"On guard!" he would cry, frightening Pedro

half to death. "This is how we shall lunge at them there at the gates of Jerusalem!"

Or again he fancied that he was preaching from the pulpit of the Cathedral of Coimbra and would cry out against the dangers of mortal sin, causing Pedro to quiver in his sandals.

Thus the slow anxious days passed for Pedro. He had made a friend of the landlord, and each morning, after bathing his sick friend with cool water, he would go out to buy food and return to cook it in the landlord's kitchen. At first Anthony could eat nothing, and Pedro prayed long into the night that his friend would not die. Apart from his grief, there was the worry about money, for the slender store which Friar Zacchary had given them for their journey was fast running out. Very soon he was forced to leave Anthony for hours at a time to go into the city looking for work. On days when he could not find it, he stood in the market place begging.

At last the day came when Anthony could sit up and eat a little, but the doctor said that it would still be a long time before he could stand on his feet. The friar tried not to show Pedro how discouraged he was, but it was hard to hide his disappointment. Here he lay helpless while all those thousands of souls outside waited to hear the Word of God, waited to be drawn into the Church of Christ.

Pedro tried to cheer him. One day he said to him, "Why, Fernando—I mean, Anthony—you will soon be preaching in the very market place where I've been begging!"

His friend smiled and made a great effort to stand on his feet. But at once he fell back onto the bed, limp and gasping.

"Look, Pedro," he said when he was able to speak, "I think it is time that we wrote to Friar Zacchary, confessing my failure."

"But sickness isn't failure!" protested Pedro.

"It was the Lord's way of showing me how ugly is my pride," sighed Anthony. "I was so proud that I thought I could be a great crusader and martyr. And look at me! Here on this bed for many months, too weak yet to stand, not a single conversion to my credit, and causing endless trouble to you and others."

"Now come," said Pedro, "you'll soon be walking again and I'll wager you, will convert the very sultan himself! I wouldn't be surprised to see you turn him into a good Friar Minor!"

Anthony laughed at that and said:

"Bring quill and parchment and write a letter for me to Friar Zacchary."

Pedro took the letter down to the wharf and put it into the hands of the very captain who had carried the two from Lisbon. He promised to see that it would be delivered to Friar Zacchary in Coimbra. His ship was to sail at dawn.

After some weeks, and just when Anthony had begun to walk again, there came a reply. Anthony held it with trembling hands, fearful of opening it, for he guessed what it might contain.

"Open it, open it!" urged Pedro, dancing about the room in his excitement.

At last the friar broke the seal and read.

"It is as I feared," he groaned, dropping down disconsolately upon the bed. "We are ordered to return at once to the friary!"

Pedro could not conceal his joy. He grinned and clapped his hands.

"What could be better?" he cried. "This is a miserable town and a miserable country! And besides, I never told you, Fernando—I mean, Anthony —that I never had any great desire to die as a martyr!"

"You surprise me," remarked the other, lifting an eyebrow and winking at Pedro.

They both laughed, but within him Anthony's heart was very sore. He could not tell which hurt him the most—the disappointment at not becoming a martyr, or his stricken pride at being forced to return to his old companions, branded as a failure.

"It will be good for my sin of pride," he told Pedro humbly.

"Better than that," cried Pedro, "it will restore you to health again! You will get well much quicker when you are out of this dreadful climate. And the fine ocean voyage will do you much good!"

"That is exactly what Friar Zacchary wrote," said Anthony dolefully. "And of course we must obey him, for we have promised our obedience to him."

The ship which carried them one cold February morning out from the port of Ceuta, bound for Lisbon, was much smaller than the one which had brought them there. There was only the captain and one sailor to man her, but she seemed sturdy enough, and Anthony and Pedro agreed to serve as additional crew. At first Anthony was awkward with the ropes and the sails, but Pedro, his gray robe hitched up about him, at once seemed as agile as a monkey and as skilled as the seaman himself. He was enjoying himself hugely, but Anthony's heart was still heavy within him. He could not rid himself of the sense of failure. This was how his first crusade was terminating—in a defeated return.

He heard the captain's voice at his elbow, saying kindly, "Sit down, Friar Anthony—here, against the stern. My mate and Brother Pedro are well able to handle things, and I know you have been ill."

Anthony was glad to take his advice. He sat, his robe drawn tightly about him, grateful for the sturdy support of the hull at his back, watching the cold, overcast sky sweep past above their heads. It was quite different from the friendly, sunny sky which had overspread their voyage from Lisbon. As he sat there, he prayed with a sad heart. He was still sick and weak, but the very fact that he could not be joyful, even in such a state, told him that he had not yet learned to be a good Friar Minor. It was well that he was returning to the friary of Coimbra to learn more, now in all humility, from Friar Zacchary and the others there. But after all, he thought, a little in self-defense, after all these men had known Father Francis himself. They had listened to his counsel, had heard his words. They had lived with him and worked with him. Oh, if only he could meet and know this Father Francis! But Francis was away off in Italy somewhere, and he, Anthony, was now speeding toward Portugal.

Speeding, indeed, was the ship, for, as the hours passed, the wind had risen steadily and the sea had grown rougher. As a cold sun set in the sky, the rain began to fall. Again he heard the captain's voice.

"This is no place for a sick man to be sitting," he said roughly. "Go below, Friar Anthony!"

The friar meekly obeyed him but, as he did so, he thought, the captain is worried, for when we came aboard his speech was gentle. He tossed himself onto his bunk and tried to sleep. But the rushing noise of the sea pounded constantly in his ears, keeping him awake, and the ship was rolling heavily. After a long time he staggered to his feet and managed, by crawling on all fours, to reach the little hatchway and climb to the deck.

There were no stars and it was so dark that he could scarcely see the three figures—the captain, with a grim hold on the helm, and the seaman and Pedro struggling to lower the sails. They came down with a heavy plop onto the deck, and the ship slowed, but only for a moment. A gale was at their back, driving them to the east with terrific speed. Huge waves rose high above them and crashed down upon the deck. The little ship tossed and rolled, trying bravely to outride the storm. But now she was taking on water and each moment was sinking lower into the sea. Anthony lay on his stomach, close to the hatchway, thinking that this would be a strange death for one who had determined to die as a martyr for Christ.

He felt someone groping beside him and then heard Pedro's voice crying into his ear, "Thank God I've found you! I was going below to bring you up."

Anthony reached out a hand and pressed the other's arm.

"Get to the mast!" cried Pedro.

Together the two crawled over the sloping, water-filled deck and reached out groping hands for the mast. The seaman was already there. Through the driving rain and swirling waters they could not see the captain clinging to his post at the helm. The water rose higher and higher about them and soon was at their waists. Then slowly the little ship tilted over on her side and they found themselves in the roaring sea, clinging to the mast.

This is the end, thought Anthony as he tried to pray.

Just then there came a crunching, groaning sound as the mast broke and floated free of the overturned, and fast-submerging, ship. The three men clung to it, certain that the captain had been lost. All of Anthony's life flashed before his eyes as he prepared to meet death. Clearly he saw his mother and father; clearly he saw Sir Juan.

Somehow he managed to raise his hand in blessing over his two companions, whispering the words of absolution. Then, as dawn was streaking the sky, he went faint and his grip on the mast loosened. He looked toward Pedro at his side and wondered, just as he lost consciousness and slipped into the sea, why Pedro should be grinning at the moment of death.

Chapter Ten

Whim of the Sea

ANTHONY awakened to the bright rays of the sun beating fiercely down upon his face. He threw an arm across his eyes, turned on his side, and stretched out a hand to feel the surface upon which he lay. He felt sand beneath his fingers, sand warmed by the sun.

He lay there trying to think where he might be and trying to recall what had befallen him. Then all the horror of the tempest came back in a flood of memory. The shipwreck, those last awful moments in the sea clinging to a mast, and then—oblivion. By some miracle he had been saved. But how?

With an effort he sat up and looked about him. He was on a white beach encircled by great dark rocks, with the sea pounding at his feet. Just then he heard a shout and looked down the beach to see Pedro and the mate hurrying toward him. Their clothing was in a terrible state. Boots and sandals were missing, and never before had he seen Pedro's hair stand out at so many wild angles.

"We let you sleep while we went to try to find food," called Pedro. "How are you feeling?"

He bent over his friend anxiously. Anthony regarded him somewhat indignantly.

"Will you tell me why on earth you were grinning happily just when we were all about to die?" he demanded.

"Oh," said Pedro, surprised. "Was I grinning? I didn't know it. It must have been because just then I stretched down and touched bottom with my feet. I knew we were near a beach. Then I looked up and behold! There it was, right under my nose!"

Weak as he was, Anthony laughed happily.

"No wonder you grinned. But I thought that our last hour had come."

"So did I," said the mate. "Then I, too, saw the land. So Brother Pedro and I each put an arm under you, just as you were sinking, and carried you to shore."

Anthony was silent for a long moment. Then he said quietly, "Thank you, my friends."

Now there came another shout, and he looked up to see the captain coming down the beach. His eyes widened with astonishment and delight.

"The captain wasn't lost!" he exclaimed.

"Not he!" laughed the mate. "He's been through worse wrecks than this. He rolled into shore on the top of a barrel right behind us."

"Thanks be to God!" exclaimed Anthony, rising to his knees. "Let us all send up a prayer of thanksgiving."

The four knelt there on the hot sand while Friar Anthony led them in a prayer that rose from full hearts. When they had finished, Anthony asked, "But where are we?"

"A whim of the sea has blown us onto the island of Sicily, Friar Anthony," replied the captain. "We are not far from the Italian coast. I know the island well. The gale blew us far off course to the east. As I clung to the helm, I kept hoping we would touch Sicily before we went down. But come. I've found a path which must lead to a village."

They followed him up the dunes and, in a short time, came to a little fishing hamlet where at a fisherman's cottage the bedraggled four found a welcome and warm food. The two Franciscans removed their sodden gray robes and Pedro washed the sea water and the sand from them, hanging them up to dry in the sunshine. Meantime, Anthony learned from their kindly host that at the nearby town of Messina there lay a well-known friary of the Friars Minor. As Pedro came in with the dry robes over his arm, his companion said, "God was very good to us, Pedro, to have cast us ashore on this spot, for we have only to walk to Messina to be among our own brothers again!"

They said warm farewells to the captain and the mate, feeling now that they were all very old friends.

"In God's Providence we shall meet again, Friar Anthony," said the captain.

Then the two seamen knelt for a blessing from the friar. Anthony made the Sign of the Cross over their heads. As they moved off to inquire how they might find passage back to Ceuta, he called after them, "I will keep you always in my prayers!"

The friary at Messina stood on a hill overlooking the sea. At once Anthony and Pedro were enchanted by its beautiful situation, the wide view of ocean and sky it commanded, and also by the grove of olive trees which surrounded it, reminding them of their beloved friary of Coimbra.

The prior, Friar Michele, welcomed them kindly, distressed at the terrors they had so recently experienced.

"You are among your own brothers here," he said, "and this shall be your home until Friar Anthony is well and strong again. Then it will be time enough to talk of your return to Portugal.

Meantime, I shall write to Friar Zacchary, telling him that you are safe here with us, and how God has miraculously preserved your lives."

Happily the two settled down to life with the Italian friars. Pedro made himself useful in a thousand ways and was happy to join once more in the joyful Franciscan singing.

Anthony celebrated Mass early each morning in the little chapel overlooking the sea. He spent long hours in prayer and, in obedience to Friar Michele, in walks along the seacoast and in the garden, letting the warm sun of Sicily restore his shattered body.

"There is nothing which will so quickly heal you," observed the prior wisely.

As he walked and prayed in solitude, Anthony grew stronger and the wound in his heart also healed. He came to see that, for all his mighty will to become a martyr, the will of God had been quite otherwise. He should have sought first to find the will of God. He must learn not only to accept it and follow it happily, but even to love it, no matter how contrary to his own desires. For it was so that Father Francis taught his friars. So had said the brothers at Coimbra. So, too, said these new brothers of Messina. Most of these had sat at the feet of the blessed Francis, learning from him. Oh, if only he could but see this Father Francis!

As the early spring days melted away and Easter came and went, Anthony knew that his health was now fully restored. It was time to return to Portugal and to the friary at Coimbra where the good Friar Zacchary waited for him and Pedro. On a sunny day in late April he rapped at Friar Michele's door.

"I have come, Father Prior," he said, "to thank you for your great kindness to Brother Pedro and me. Thanks to you, I am quite well again, and whenever you wish to arrange it, we are ready to return to our friary in Coimbra."

Friar Michele looked up with a smile from the letter he had been reading.

"Here is news, Friar Anthony!" he cried joyously. "Our Father Francis has returned from his mission to Egypt where, in truth, he had hoped to die as a martyr—"

Anthony blinked and put a hand out on the table for support.

"What's the matter?" asked the other, anxiously. "You look faint. You are still not well, it seems."

"It's nothing," smiled Anthony. "Only—only I was so glad to hear that Father Francis had wanted to die as a martyr for Christ."

"Oh, *that!*" exclaimed Michele, brushing the idea away with his hand. "He's always wanted *that!* Didn't you know it?"

Anthony shook his head. Michele threw his own back and laughed heartily.

"It's all very amusing," he said, "for our blessed Father Francis went out to Egypt to join a crusade which was besieging the Saracens in Damietta. He tried his best to get martyred. But the word has run around that, the harder he tried, and the harder he preached to the Saracens, the more they liked him! They did not want to become Christians but they *did* love Father Francis, as everyone does. He even bearded the great sultan in his golden tent and proclaimed Christ, hoping to get his head chopped off—as many another Christian head has been chopped off, for less! But the sultan only smiled and loaded him with rich gifts. He begged Father Francis to remain with him forever. Poor Father Francis was terribly disappointed."

"I should think he might have been," sighed Anthony sympathetically.

"So, having plunged his head right into the mouth of the lion, and having done his best to give his life for Christ, he has come home feeling that he is a total failure. But he left the whole Saracen country loving him!"

Friar Michele burst into another roar of laughter. Then he leaned across the table and pointed a finger at Anthony.

"The truth is," he said seriously, "that no one can see Francis without loving him. And I think the secret is that Francis himself loves everyone! No one—not even a Saracen—would do him harm. The joke is that Francis is quite unaware of all this and regards himself as the most unworthy of men."

Anthony sighed again.

"Oh, how I should love to see him!" he exclaimed.

"And so you shall!" cried Michele. "For this letter which I was just reading calls us all up to Assisi to attend a General Chapter of the Friars Minor. And you and Brother Pedro shall go along with us!"

Anthony's face lit up with a smile but darkened almost at once.

"But, Father Prior, how can we?" he protested. "We owe our obedience to Friar Zacchary in Coimbra, and we must return there as soon as possible."

"You will probably see Friar Zacchary at the General Chapter. It is calling in all the Friars Minor everywhere, from all over the world!" exclaimed the other. "There you can join him and all your brothers of Coimbra and return to Portugal with them!"

Anthony was overjoyed, and so, too, was Pedro.

In a few days the little company set forth to make the long journey—first by ship to the mainland, and then on foot up through Italy from the south and across many long miles to the hills of Umbria where Assisi lies.

Anthony was amazed, as they went along, to see the vast number of friars converging upon the roads. They seemed like a mighty army, these gray-robed friars, growing larger every day. All were marching toward Assisi, marching to see their Father Francis whom they loved and followed. By the time they reached Assisi, the army numbered more than 3,000. They had come not alone from Italy, but from many distant countries.

The little city itself was too small to hold the vast

assemblage, so the friars converged upon the great plain stretching far below Assisi, which rises like a dream upon the high hilltop above it. Its towers and its battlements seem to pierce the clouds of an endlessly blue and beautiful sky. There, on the plain below, stands the little church which was the birthplace of the Order of Friars Minor, named by Francis the Portiuncula, meaning the "Little Portion" of land which he had begged for a church for his first twelve friars.

Back on this summer day of the year 1221, Anthony and Pedro awaited their turn in the crowd to make their prayers within the tiny church. But the numbers were so great that somehow they got separated from their brothers of Messina.

The moment that Anthony set foot within the Portiuncula, he knew he was in a holy place. Something caught at his heart and held it. He longed for the moment when he would see Father Francis face to face.

The friars had erected little shelters of reeds and boughs over the plain where they slept as the Chapter went on day after day. There were conferences and meetings to discuss plans for the future of the order. But the leaders, those who were priors, and the provincials who governed whole provinces, stood closest to Father Francis. For days poor Anthony, a new friar and a stranger unknown to the thousands, could not come near him. He was too shy to push his way forward.

Everywhere he and Pedro looked for their friends from Messina, but the crowd had swallowed them up. Pedro, distracted, ran around searching for Friar Zacchary and the others from Coimbra. No one had seen them; no one knew whether they were there or not. Anthony and Pedro felt terribly alone.

Finally, on the last day of the Chapter, as Anthony stood, discouraged, on the rim of the crowd, it parted suddenly to make way for a frail figure in the familiar rough robe. Anthony wondered who it could be. The face was hidden by the gray cowl which covered the head.

All at once the figure paused and turned. Anthony found himself gazing into a thin face which seemed illumined as by a candle burning somewhere within. Never before had he seen such love and compassion looking out from human eyes. The eyes were large and dark, and the features regular.

For a brief moment the eyes of the two men met—Francis and Anthony—and spoke to each other. Then the crowd surged between them, calling, "A blessing, Father Francis! A blessing!"

The slight figure raised a hand and slowly made the Sign of the Cross over them. With a heart lighter than air, Anthony knelt in the dust to receive it.

Then the figure moved on and was lost to sight.

Chapter Eleven

CHARM OF A VOICE

WHAT had amazed Anthony about the face of
Father Francis was that, for all its marks of penance
and fasting, its finely drawn outline was yet so
youthful and joyous. He had always thought of
Father Francis as an older man. But the slender
leader did not seem much older than himself. And
Anthony was not yet twenty-six. Pedro, too, had
been astounded by the youth of that gentle face with

its remarkable eyes. Francis was actually thirty-nine.

The two strangers sat there near the road, watching thousands of friars pass by on their way home. They scanned each face but could see neither their brothers of Messina nor their brothers of Coimbra. But Anthony was no longer disturbed. With the blessing of Francis, a wondrous peace had come upon him. Now he had no other wish than to do the will of God, and somehow he knew that soon it would be revealed to him.

As the last of the friars passed, one among them paused and looked uncertainly at the two. He was a tall, dignified figure, with a kindly face browned by the sun and thick gray hair. Anthony at once knew him for a man of authority and sprang to his feet.

"Your pardon, Father Friar," he said bowing, "if we seem to linger here. But we have lost our companions and are strangers from Portugal. We do not know where to go."

The tall friar eyed them kindly and smiled, but Anthony was also aware of the keen gaze with which he studied them.

"I am Friar Gratian," he said, "provincial of the Province of the Romagna." Now the Romagna was a wide territory which embraced all of Lombardy.

Anthony introduced himself and his companion and briefly told their story. Friar Gratian did not hesitate. Quickly he said, "I would like very much to welcome you into my province. I have need of more friars, and just such men as you."

Anthony smiled and bowed again.

"You honor us, Friar Gratian. Gladly would we accept but that we feel bound by obedience to return to our friary of Coimbra where Friar Zacchary awaits us."

"If you like, I will obtain permission for your release from Coimbra."

Anthony and Pedro looked at one another. Each read in the other's eyes the desire to accept Friar Gratian's proposal. Together they turned to the older man and exclaimed as in one breath, "Gladly will we come with you, Friar Gratian!"

Soon they were walking along with a dozen other friars, all happily discussing the Chapter General. As they pressed northward into the Romagna and toward the city of Bologna where lay their friary, they often broke into song in which Pedro lustily joined. Anthony seized every occasion to ply his new companions with questions about Father Francis.

"Whence comes his great peace?" he kept asking.

The answer was always the same. "He finds his strength and peace in the mountains," they would say, "where he often goes alone to fast, to pray, and to meditate."

Anthony reflected how frequently our Lord, when He was upon earth, had gone into the mountains to be alone and to pray. Now he wanted with all his heart to do the same.

One day, when they were nearing the end of their journey, Friar Gratian fell into step beside Anthony.

"The Friars Minor are now a large army, Friar Anthony, but as yet we have few priests among us to serve the poor. You are one of these. I've been thinking of a lonely little hermitage of ours at the top of a mountain, Monte Paolo. Six of the brothers are now living there, but they have no priest to celebrate Mass. How would you like to be among them for a while? It seems to me that you need a time of quiet and prayer after all you have been through."

It was as though Friar Gratian had read his heart. Anthony's face was all smiles as he exclaimed:

"I should be most happy, Friar Gratian!"

"I shall have need of Brother Pedro in Bologna," went on the other. Then, as he saw the look of dismay which passed over Anthony's face he added quickly, "But it won't be long before you will be working together again."

Pedro himself was rather pleased with the decision. The idea of a solitary mountain top, with no excitement save the whispering of the wind and the murmur of a mountain brook, did not greatly appeal to him. He much preferred to be in the busy, lively city of Bologna which he had heard was thronged with students from all over the world who were there to attend its famous university.

At last Anthony drew courage to ask Friar Gratian himself certain questions about Father Francis and his method of prayer.

"He loves our Lord with a consuming love," said Gratian softly. "And he has great devotion to our Lady. But he has a particularly great and tender love for our Lord as a little Child. When he speaks of the Christ Child, his whole face seems to be alight. Every Christmas Eve he has the scene of the Nativity enacted in a mountain grove of evergreen trees. All is there as it should be—the manger and the Babe, the ox, and the ass. People flock from far and near to see it and to hear him preach on the love of the Christ Child for all mankind."

Anthony felt very happy. As far removed as he believed himself to be from the holy founder of the order, here was something indeed which they shared in common. In his heart he blessed little Inez with her crutches, who long ago had taught him to love the Christ Child.

In their talks it never occurred to him to tell Friar Gratian that he, too, knew how to preach. His experience in Assisi had made him feel small and unimportant. Back in Portugal everyone knew him as the descendant of the great Godfrey de Bouillon, and as the son of the governor of Lisbon. They knew him as a scholar and a preacher. Here no one knew him at all. All those thousands of simple friars had seemed to be far better and holier than he. And when he once looked upon the face of Francis he had known that he was looking upon the face of a saint. He sighed and sadly confided his thoughts to Pedro.

"But you," exclaimed Pedro in astonishment, "are a nobleman, a scholar, and a great preacher! How many of those rustics, do you think, know as much as you? How many of them can preach as you can?"

"What is scholarship? What is preaching?" asked Anthony dejectedly. "It is holiness and closeness to God which count."

"Well," replied Pedro cheerfully, "you can come very close to God upon that mountain top you're going to. From all I hear, it is so high that it touches the skies. How could you get closer to God than that?"

Pedro looked so serious when he said this that Anthony had to laugh. It was wonderful how Pedro could always cheer him up when he felt sad.

The months that Anthony spent at the little hermitage on the mountain top brought him all that he had hoped for. Each day, after he had celebrated Mass for the brothers, he insisted upon washing the dishes and cleaning the house. Then he would retire to a cave in the rocks for prayer. He came to love the solitude and the beauty of the mountains and the presence of God he felt in them. He hoped he would never have to leave them.

Then one evening, when returning from his cave, he was startled to see a familiar red head looming above the high green bush which grew at the hermitage door.

"Pedro!" he cried as the other ran to meet him, grinning from ear to ear. They flung their arms about each other.

"I've come on orders from the provincial himself," explained Pedro importantly. "Friar Gratian says that I must bring you at once to meet him in the city of Forli!"

"Forli?" asked Anthony, puzzled. "Why Forli?"

"Because it is there, at the church of San Mercuriale, that several friars will be ordained to the priesthood. Friar Gratian wants us there. What a lark!" he added, jumping up and down.

"Lark?" asked Anthony, almost doubling with laughter. "That's the first time I ever heard an ordination called a lark!"

Early the next morning the two joyously set forth, making their way down the mountainside which was wearing its first fresh green of early spring. The year was 1222.

In Forlí they easily found their way to the church upon which friars from many sections were now converging. On the steps they encountered Friar Gratian, who greeted them warmly.

"So you have completed your retreat upon the mountain top, Friar Anthony!" he exclaimed. "You look better for it. Now I shall have to think of a new post for you."

"I am here to do whatever you wish of me, Friar Gratian," answered Anthony with a smile.

"This is a wonderful day for the Friars Minor," continued the provincial. "Think of welcoming seven new priests into the order!"

"Congratulations!" smiled Anthony.

"We are the guests here of his lordship, the bishop," went on the other, "and, after the ceremony, we are all invited to luncheon. Following that, a sermon on the ordination will be delivered."

Anthony could see how proud and happy the good provincial was that his friars should be so honored. As the two bowed and moved away to enter the church, Friar Gratian's eyes followed Anthony. An extraordinary young priest, he thought, this young friar from Portugal, but as yet I know little about him. I shall have to find work for him. But what?

Anthony and Pedro, still feeling like strangers, shyly took their seats in the rear of the church. Before them, and mingled with their own brothers, they saw many strange friars who were clad in white robes.

"Those are men of the Order of Preachers," whispered Pedro, "which was founded by the holy Dominic. They are trained especially to preach. It is said they are marvelously eloquent."

Anthony regarded them curiously.

When the beautiful ceremony of ordination was over, the two followed the throng to a large hall

where the luncheon was to be served. The bishop
and Friar Gratian sat on a platform at one end of the
room. Anthony and Pedro took seats at a table in
the rear. The Friars Preachers, in their white robes,
as honored guests, occupied the front tables. Behind
them sat the gray-robed friars of Francis.

When the meal was over, Friar Gratian arose to
announce that the ordination sermon would be delivered by a famed orator of the Friars Preachers.
But when he called upon the man to come forward
and take his place upon the platform, everyone was
surprised to hear a voice from the foremost table
saying, "Your pardon, Friar Gratian, but I did not
have time to prepare a sermon. I beg you to hold me
excused."

Friar Gratian could scarcely believe his ears. He
flushed and stammered and looked in great embar-
rassment toward the bishop.

Now that is too bad, thought Anthony, to have
our good provincial so embarrassed.

The bishop leaned forward and whispered a few
words to the provincial, who now came down from
the platform and moved in and out among the tables
of Friars Preachers. He asked first this one and then
that one to assume the task. One by one all shook
their heads, each saying that he was not prepared.
At last poor Friar Gratian was forced to go among
his own men to make the same request. But the
Friars Minor, not trained to the pulpit as were the
Preachers, were all too frightened to dare attempt a

sermon, unprepared, in the presence of the great
bishop. By this time the worried provincial, hot and
flushed, looked as though he wished the ground
would open and swallow him up. Then suddenly,
his eye fell upon Anthony.

"Friar Anthony," he called, almost in despair,
"will you deliver the sermon?"

Anthony went white. This was the last thing he
had expected. He sat there trembling and was about
to shake his head when Pedro punched him under
the table.

"Go on," he whispered fiercely. "You can do it
better than anyone!"

Anthony looked into his provincial's face, and
his heart was moved at the real distress he saw there.
He rose unsteadily to his feet, his brain in a whirl.

"I am here to obey you in all things, Friar Gratian, and if you wish me to speak, I shall try, although I have made no preparation."

Slowly he followed the provincial up the long
aisle between the tables, trying to form his thoughts
into a pattern. But all was confusion. As he passed,
he heard the wondering murmurs among his own
brothers. He saw the amused smiles upon the faces
of the Friars Preachers. He was terribly frightened.
And frightened, too, was Friar Gratian. Supposing
that this new, strange friar from Portugal should
disgrace him, and the Friars Minor, before the
bishop?

Somehow Anthony reached the platform, bowed

to the bishop and to his provincial, and turned to his audience. In utter panic within, he bent his head a moment in prayer, asking the Child Jesus to help him—even as he had asked Him long ago when he first began to preach in Coimbra. His knees were trembling now just as violently as they had trembled then.

Aloud he quoted to the assembly, "Christ became obedient unto death, even unto the death of the Cross."

It was this thought which sustained him, for never before had he undertaken so difficult an act of obedience. Then, in a weak voice, he fumbled for the first words of his sermon. But suddenly his mind cleared and all at once his voice took on strength and the words poured forth. To honor the seven who had just been ordained, he preached on the dignity of the priesthood. The charm of his voice, the power of his ideas, took hold of them and would not let them go. Not a murmur, not a rustle was heard in that hushed assemblage. The bishop was now leaning forward in his chair to catch every word.

When the preacher had finished, he bowed again to the bishop and to the provincial and walked quietly back to his table at the end of the long room. But the spell still held them. No one moved. Then all at once a wild applause broke out, and he saw the bishop coming toward him. Pedro was grinning as never before.

"My son, you have a great gift," said the bishop

as Anthony knelt to kiss the ring. "I hope that we shall hear you preach many times!"

Friar Gratian was right behind him, and the brothers thought he had never looked so happy. Embracing Anthony, he cried, "I was wondering what on earth to do with you! Now I know. You shall be my first preacher. You shall preach in all the Romagna and bring many souls back to Christ!"

From then on, Anthony and Pedro lived in the friary at Bologna. From there, Anthony went forth to begin his great work as a preacher in Italy. Wherever he went, crowds hastened to hear him. The good news of the new preacher traveled fast and reached the delighted Father Francis in Assisi. He sent his blessing to Anthony and asked him to preach, not alone in the Romagna, but also throughout all Italy. He also asked him to teach the young novices in Bologna and to prepare them for the priesthood. Anthony was not yet thirty.

About that time Father Francis was greatly worried about a heresy which had taken hold of the people in the north, especially in the city of Rimini. They had been led away from God by false teachers. Anthony was sent to them to try to win them back to the Faith.

He and Pedro walked the long roads to reach at length a city which at once turned its back upon them. No one in Rimini welcomed the friars in their poor, gray robes. Many laughed at them as they passed. But Anthony found his way to the market place and began to preach. A few idlers stood about listening from curiosity. Gradually the number grew. When Anthony saw that he had an audience, he began to talk to them of Christ in the Blessed Sacrament.

That was too much for the heretics of Rimini. They roared out their unbelief and made jibes at the speaker. One ruffian pushed his way close to him and spat in the preacher's face.

"We want no filthy friars in this town," he cried. "Get out!"

One by one the crowd dispersed, flinging its jibes and its curses at Anthony's head. All at once he and Pedro found themselves facing an empty square. Never before, as a preacher, had Anthony met defeat. Utterly discouraged, he sat down upon a stone and put his head into his hands.

"Come," said Pedro cheerfully, "do not feel so badly. These people have hearts of stone. They would not listen to the Lord Himself!"

But Anthony would not look up. Poor Pedro did not know what to do. Then suddenly he had an idea.

"You know that pretty river we passed near the edge of the city?" he asked.

The other nodded dolefully.

"Let us walk there and sit by the stream. It will be quiet and cool, and there we shall not see those awful people!"

Reluctantly Anthony followed his friend to the

river bank. He could not remember when he had felt so sad. This gift that God had given him—the gift to preach—had suddenly been taken from him. He had failed his Father Francis; he had failed Friar Gratian. The heretics of Rimini would not listen to him. They would remain heretics. So many souls lost to God—all through his failure! Sadly he looked down into the rippling waters of the river at his feet.

Then a strange thing happened. A little fish stuck his head out of the water, then dove again, and came up just at Anthony's feet. He stayed there, fluttering his fins, and seemed to be looking up at the friar. Anthony smiled and began to talk to him, calling him Brother Fish, just as Father Francis had taught his friars to address all of God's creatures. Then another little fish came and joined the first. Anthony spoke to them tenderly about the love of God for all His creatures. Now there were a dozen fish at his feet. Soon there came a great splashing as a whole shoal of them swam into sight and clustered there below the friar. Each had his head cocked above the water, listening attentively to the sermon.

Anthony talked gently on to them, praising God Who had given them life. He was quite unaware that a number of people had gathered silently behind him to watch the strange sight. A boy who had been playing near the river had seen it and had run to tell others.

At last the friar raised his hand in blessing over

the creatures of the water who had listened to him when men would not. The waters of the river rippled gaily as the little fish took their departure and swam away. A silence hung upon the air. The charm of the voice still held the audience spellbound. All at once Anthony heard a rough voice behind him and turned.

"Come to the market place again tomorrow, Friar Anthony," it said, "and we will listen to you. For truly we have never seen so great a wonder!"

Anthony, from the bank, looked down upon the speaker. To his surprise he saw that it was the same man who had, earlier that day, heaped the worst insult upon him.

Chapter Twelve

ANTHONY OF PADUA

When Anthony and Pedro again took to the road their hearts were happy because they had left many converts among the heretics of Rimini. But a change had come over Pedro. Ever since he had seen the fishes of the river gather at Anthony's feet he had been much quieter. Several times Anthony had caught him looking at him with a sort of awe upon his face instead of the usual grin.

"Now stop all that nonsense," Anthony said to

him as they walked along, "and don't continue to look at me as though I were some strange stuffed animal in a museum."

That made Pedro laugh. The grin reappeared.

"Just because the good God wished to soften the hearts of the heretics," went on Anthony, "is no reason why you should regard me as anything extraordinary. I had nothing whatever to do with it."

"Well," said Pedro, "that you could make those fish listen to you did give me rather a shock. I had always thought of you as just plain Fernando—a boy I had sat next to in school."

"And so that's all I am. Just plain Fernando-Anthony, a boy you sat next to in school," replied the other. Then he added softly, "And we are still boys in school, for there is yet so much to learn."

Soon the two were talking over their boyhood in Lisbon, and Pedro had fallen into an imitation of Old Lopez. He swaggered down the road ahead of Anthony, his stomach thrust out, and rolling from side to side in a sailor's gait.

"Come right this way, my mates," he said in a gruff voice. "Old Lopez will show you what a sweet life he has in store for you. You've no idea what sport it is to see people walk the plank."

He sounded so much like the old pirate that Anthony had to sit down by the roadside to laugh.

"I think that if you were to give that imitation before the heretics whom we are soon to meet, it would attract more people than any sermon I could preach," said his friend.

Thus, to Anthony's relief, Pedro had become himself again.

They journeyed the long miles over the high Alps and into France where Father Francis had sent Anthony to preach to the heretics of Toulouse. After a time he was so successful there and converted so many that people now began to speak of him as "the Hammer of Heresy."

But Anthony kept wishing that he could see Father Francis once more. If only he would again give me his blessing, he thought, I'm sure I could do better. But Francis remained far away in Assisi.

About this time there was to be a meeting in Provence of all the friars who were in France. Anthony and Pedro journeyed there to attend it. The brothers wanted to hear the famous preacher speak, so Anthony stood humbly before them and spoke to them about Christ the King. While he was preaching, suddenly one of the friars, a holy man named Monaldo, chanced to look back at the doorway. There, to his amazement, he saw the figure of Father Francis himself, raised in the air, with his hands extended in blessing.

Anthony was very happy when Monaldo told him of this. "I had been praying for his blessing," he said simply.

The holy founder, who was far away in Assisi,

had sent his spirit over the many miles and across the Alps to bless his friar.

For a time in France, Anthony and Pedro lived in the friary of Montpellier where Anthony had been sent to instruct the novices. Pedro attended the classes, although there was much he did not understand, for Anthony was teaching advanced theology. Besides, there was a brother in the friary, one Louis, who distracted Pedro during the lectures. He was restless and looked unhappy, and he was forever gazing out of the window while Anthony was speaking. It bothered Pedro.

Now everyone there knew that, while the brothers were studying each afternoon, Friar Anthony went to his cell to work on a book he was writing on the Psalms of the Bible. He had begun it some years before, working on it whenever he could find the time. He had put his heart into it, hoping that it would help others to understand the Psalms better. Everyone knew that it would be a wonderful book when it was finished. Day after day Anthony labored on it with quill and parchment, in the fine, careful writing he had learned long before in the cathedral school of Lisbon.

But between that and his lectures, and the many hours he spent in prayer, he began to look thin and tired, for he gave himself no time to rest. Pedro was worried about him.

One hot summer afternoon, Pedro took courage and knocked at the door of Anthony's cell.

"It must be very warm for you in there," he called, "working at your manuscript. You've been at it now for several hours. If you don't look out, you'll turn into a book yourself! Why not come and take a walk with me?"

He hadn't much hope that Anthony would listen but, to his surprise, the other opened the door a crack and nodded, smiling. The friar turned back to his table to pile the manuscript neatly together and to close the window, lest the wind blow the parchments about. As he lovingly fingered them and saw how much of the book was now completed, he uttered a little sigh of pleasure. Many hours of labor over the years had gone into it, but now, happily, it was almost finished.

Together the two walked out into the hills and found a place in the cool green shade of the trees. They sat there for an hour or more until Anthony said, "It's almost time for Vespers. We must start walking back."

When they reached the friary, they went at once to the chapel where the service was about to begin. Perhaps an hour later, Anthony opened the door of his cell, happy in the thought of his manuscript and that in only a few more days it would be completed. He shut the door behind him and looked toward the table. To his amazement the manuscript was gone.

He looked everywhere for it. He searched the bare little cell from corner to corner. He saw that the window still remained closed. The parchments could not have blown away. Neither could they have taken wings and flown away! Frightened and breathless, he ran to find the prior. Perhaps Father Prior had wished to see the work upon which he had been so long engaged. But Father Prior only shook his head. He was as mystified as was Anthony himself over the strange disappearance, and he grieved to see his friar's distress.

When the brothers were sitting down to supper, the prior addressed them: "Friar Anthony has lost his manuscript. If one of you has borrowed it, let him please come forward."

No one stirred. Then, after a moment, the silence was broken by the voice of a young novice in the rear.

"Brother Louis is missing at supper tonight, Father Prior."

As the meal continued, all watched the door anxiously, hoping to see Brother Louis appear. He did not come. When supper was over, Father Prior sent the brothers out to search for him. But Brother Louis had vanished as though the ground had swallowed him up. At last a farmer who lived nearby said that he had seen a friar hurrying along the road early that afternoon with a bundle under his arm. It was now plain that Brother Louis had run away.

"I never trusted him anyway," whispered Pedro to Anthony. "He did not listen to your lectures. He was always looking out of the window. And now he has gone off with your precious manuscript!"

"Hush," said Anthony. "We do not know that he took it. We must not condemn poor, unhappy Brother Louis. Worse than the loss of the manuscript is the loss of his vocation! Let us go into the chapel and pray for him."

Anthony prayed with all his heart that God would save Brother Louis. And with all his heart, too, he asked the Child Jesus to restore his manuscript.

"You know," he whispered, "how many years I have worked on it. Will You now let that labor be lost? And yet—if it is Your will—let it be lost! In the eyes of our heavenly Father it can seem like only a little thing anyway—like a mere toy in the hands of one of His children. He is very good to us. He gives us such toys to play with. I have loved this toy. You, as a little Child, understand how God's children love their toys and how they grieve when they are lost. So, if it should be pleasing to our heavenly Father, please restore it to me!"

Far away, and many miles from the friary, Brother Louis sat resting on the bank of a wide river which flowed past him on its way to the great capital of France. Anthony's manuscript lay at his side. He was taking it to Paris where he would sell it and claim that he, himself, had written it. Some rich monastery would be sure to buy it, for those who knew about such matters had said that it was a great masterpiece. Brother Louis would become famous.

As he sat there, thinking of these things, suddenly a wild wind arose and whipped the river into a frenzy. All at once Brother Louis saw a horrible monster rising from its depths. It advanced upon him with burning eyes, waving its long arms.

"Oh, wicked brother!" cried the monster. "Return. Return at once to the friary and restore his manuscript to Friar Anthony! Otherwise you shall be destroyed!"

In terror Louis scrambled to his feet and set out at a run for Montpellier. He arrived at dawn and fell, gasping, at the door of Anthony's cell. The friar heard his sobs and opened the door. He leaned down and lifted up Brother Louis and embraced him.

"Much more than the return of the manuscript is your own return to the friary!" he exclaimed joyously. "Your soul is more precious to God than any book. Come inside and tell me what it was that troubled you here."

So Brother Louis sat down with him and, between his tears, poured out his story. He had wanted to become a great scholar and preacher. He had wished to be like Anthony himself. But he found it so hard to study. It would take him too long. Then an evil spirit had whispered to him that if he stole Anthony's manuscript, he could pass himself off as a scholar in Paris and obtain a high position.

"Please forgive me, Friar Anthony!" he implored.

"Freely do I forgive you!" smiled Anthony.
"And what is more, from now on I shall teach you
myself in private lessons. You will find how easy
it is to learn. Then soon we shall have a scholar to be
proud of in our dear Brother Louis!"

Pedro and the others felt sure that only Anthony's
prayers had restored the lost manuscript. So from
that time onward, whenever anything was lost in
the friary, the brothers went to Anthony and asked
him to pray for its return. The lost object was always found. This news spread beyond the walls of
the friary, and soon a stream of people came daily
to beg for the friar's prayers. The Child Jesus always listened, understanding how the human heart
could grieve over the loss of a "toy," whether it
was the rare jewel of some great lady or the little
basket of a peasant girl.

Now that the book on the Psalms was finished,
Anthony went out more frequently to preach. The
crowds that came to hear him were so great that
no church could contain them. He was forced to
preach in the open fields. It was now widely known
that this young friar could perform great wonders
through prayer, and he was besieged on every hand
by the poor, the sick, and the unhappy. But his heart
rested in Assisi, where he longed to go to receive
once more the blessing of Francis.

Then one day in the year 1226 he lay within his
cell stricken with grief. The news had just reached
France that the beloved founder of the Friars Minor,

sick and worn from serving the poor, had died in Assisi. Now it was too late for that blessing. But surely, if he prayed to him, Father Francis would bless him from heaven! It was said that all of Italy mourned the passing of one whom all proclaimed to be a saint. With heavy hearts Anthony and Pedro set out for Assisi where lay the body of Father Francis.

By this time Pope Gregory IX had heard a great deal about young Friar Anthony and sent for him to preach to the people of Rome during Holy Week. Again the crowds which flocked to his sermons were so vast that the people were forced to follow him into the open fields.

In the throng that hastened to hear him on Easter Sunday there were many strangers from faraway lands who had come to Rome for the Holy Season. Most of them did not speak, or understand, the language of Italy. But it was enough for them to see this great preacher and worker of wonders, even if they could not understand what he was saying.

Anthony looked out upon the throng and saw the number of strangers. They were there from England, from Germany, from France, and Spain. All were straining to understand him. He bent his head in prayer. When he resumed the sermon, an extraordinary thing happened. Each one in that great assemblage seemed to hear his own tongue, and the heart of each was filled with the beautiful thoughts which Anthony uttered.

"This is the friar," the crowd whispered, "who cures the sick, who finds lost objects, and who—or so it is reported—has even raised the dead to life!"

They pressed upon him to take him by the hand, begging for his blessing, and even trying to cut off little pieces of his robe to carry away. Pedro was anxious. He gathered a group of strong young friars about him, and together they formed a guard for Anthony, going with him wherever he went, and protecting him from the crowd.

Some weeks later Anthony and Pedro were glad to be again alone on the road.

"Since we left Lisbon we have seen many fair cities in Italy and France," said Anthony. "But I have the strangest feeling that the city we now approach will be the one we shall like best of all."

"Padua?" asked Pedro, incredulously.

The other nodded.

"Why, Fernando—I mean, Anthony—Padua is said to be fairly running with sinners! That is why the Father-General is sending you there."

"Running with sinners, yes," smiled Anthony, "but not running with heretics. The Paduans have the gift of faith, thank God! That is why everyone says they are such happy people. We shall not see any of those gloomy heretics about here, thank goodness!"

"Surely you don't prefer sinners to heretics?"

"I do," said Anthony serenely, "for a sinner, if

he has the Christian faith, can always repent and reform. Whereas a heretic . . ."

He broke off and became lost in thought.

"It is said that the people of Padua are very gay and very rich," remarked Pedro. "It seems they like nothing better than to have a high old time!"

"That's because they have too much money," replied Anthony. "Now we must try to see that less of it goes to their clothes and their pleasures and more of it to the poor."

It was a lovely spring day when they passed for the first time through the stone gates of the city. Everywhere they were greeted by laughter, and song, and flowers. Soon they were walking past the great university for which Padua was famous. From its doors there poured forth the carefree youth of many lands, all joking and laughing among themselves. Pedro smiled happily. The scene reminded him of schooldays in Lisbon when he, and Sancho, and Fernando had raced down the hill together with Jingo barking at their heels. As the two made their way to the house of the Friars Minor, people on the streets smiled at them, calling out a welcome to the gray-robed strangers.

Within a few days these very people were filling the churches and the public squares to hear Anthony preach. Many repented of their sins and besieged him to hear their confessions.

"They are like a lot of children," smiled Anthony.

Within six weeks the whole city was transformed. Money and food poured into the hands of the hungry poor who were Anthony's especial charge. The friar came to love these gay, openhearted people as he had never loved any others, and they, in turn, loved him.

Before his arrival Padua had the custom of casting into prison the poor who could not pay their debts. Anthony prevailed upon the city fathers to change this law. He helped the debtors to find employment so they could pay off their debts. He helped everyone—the poor and the rich, the high and the lowly.

About this time the Pope wished to bestow some special honors upon the famous preacher, as did also his own Order of Friars Minor. But Anthony implored them just to permit him to serve the people and to preach. At length he had his way. And when they asked him where he wished most to live and to work, he replied, "In Padua, at the friary of St. Mary's!"

From there he set forth on many mission journeys into the far cities of the north, into the cities of the heretics.

One stormy winter day, when he and Pedro had crossed the mountains in the snow barefooted, in their open sandals, they came at last to a castle whose lord was a friend of Anthony's. They rapped at the gate to beg shelter for the night. The lord welcomed them gladly and had them sit down to dinner with him.

"You are tired, Friar Anthony," he said, when the meal was over. "Allow me to conduct you to the room which has been prepared for you. It is at the top of the castle where it is quieter and where you can rest better than anywhere else."

Pedro was to sleep in another section of the castle. Anthony said good night to him and followed his host up the winding stair which led to the room in the tower.

"You will go to rest at once?" pressed his host, who thought his guest looked pale and ill.

"After a few prayers, my good friend," Anthony assured him.

Much later that night the lord of the castle was awakened by a strange brilliance in his room. It seemed to come from the corridor beyond his curtained doorway. Was the castle on fire? Alarmed, he rose from his bed and pushed aside the curtain. The hall, to be sure, was lighted as by a hundred torches, but the source of the light was not visible. Then the good man saw that it shone brightest at the foot of the tower stairs. Perhaps his friend's room was on fire!

Quickly he mounted and drew aside the curtain over the doorway. What he saw there he was never afterward able to mention without falling to his knees.

Anthony stood in the center of the room, holding a beautiful little Child in his arms. Around the small head there gleamed a brilliant aureole as bright as the sun, and from it the light was streaming everywhere, through the room and down the stairs. Tenderly the friar held the smiling Child, bending his head above Him. As the lord of the castle gazed, speechless, the Child lifted a small hand and stroked the friar's thin face.

The lord tiptoed softly down the stairs. But he slept no more that night. In the morning he drew Anthony aside and whispered to him what he had seen.

"I beg of you, my good friend," urged the other earnestly, "not to speak of this to anyone."

"But I saw the Child Jesus Himself!" protested his friend. "It was a great miracle!"

Upon the friar's urging he promised to keep the secret until after Anthony's death, a promise he faithfully fulfilled.

When Pedro and Anthony returned to Padua, they found the city harassed by the tyrant of a neighboring castle who was called "Ezzelino the Ferocious." He hated Padua and did his best to make the city miserable, even to carrying off some of its best-known citizens and holding them for ransom. Anthony risked his life, going back and forth as an emissary to the tyrant, pleading for mercy for the city he loved. Everyone thought that Ezzelino would surely kill him. But the friar was not afraid.

As the summer of 1231 advanced, Anthony, who was not yet thirty-six, began to feel his body failing him. He reflected silently that he had caused it to suffer great hardships in this odd crusade upon which he had embarked for his Lord. How much could one expect of a mere body anyway? He had forced it to walk endless miles over the hills and mountains, and in the worst sort of weather. He had fasted and had prayed through the long nights without sleep. Now Pedro watched over him anxiously. But the son of the governor of Lisbon knew that his days were numbered.

Just beyond Padua, in the countryside, lay the estate of a nobleman, a great friend of the Friars Minor. With the hot summer upon them, he invited Anthony and some of the brothers to come and stay in the green woods of his estate. They were glad to leave the hot city and to build shelters for themselves under the trees.

Pedro, seeing that his friend had grown so weak, undertook to build the shelter for Anthony. He selected a spot under a tall, beautiful walnut tree which Anthony greatly admired. Then he built his own little shelter nearby.

The brothers were very happy there in the woods. One day a messenger came from the friary with a letter for Anthony.

"It's from Lisbon!" cried Pedro, handing it to his friend and dancing up and down in his excitement.

Anthony broke the seal and read. At last he laid down the letter and said softly, "All is well, Pedro, my friend. The letter is from Sir Juan. He writes to say that my mother and father have died. I thank God that they died peacefully and within a short time of each other! Nor do I grieve, for I know that I shall see them soon in heaven. A good cousin of mine has inherited Castle de Bulhom. It is well. He will do much better, as its lord, than I would ever have done!"

Pedro did not know what to say, but his heart was aching within him.

"What pleases me greatly," went on Anthony, smiling, "is that Sir Juan has married a noble lady of Lisbon and is very happy. He speaks of journeying to Italy with her in the fall to see us." He paused a moment and then added quietly, "I shall not be here at that time, Pedro."

His friend looked away and began fidgeting with the cord at his waist to hide his tears.

"Sir Juan still addresses me as 'young fellow,'" laughed Anthony. "One would think that I had never grown up!"

But Pedro would not look up.

"I'll tell you what," went on his friend cheerfully. "I will write a letter to the Father-General, who has promised to grant me anything I want. I will ask him to send you back to Portugal upon my death. You can carry letters to Sir Juan and others for me. The Friars Minor have a new house in Lisbon. I shall ask him to send you there where you can be near your parents."

Pedro lifted his head and tried to smile. But the old grin had vanished.

"And then," continued Anthony, "you will be living near the port and can be happy again sniffing all those terrible odors!"

At this he held his nose and made a face. Pedro was at last forced to laugh. The grin reappeared.

Anthony lay there, gazing far up into the green, whispering leaves of the great walnut tree. They spoke to him of the love of God. Those who looked into his face felt that the Child Jesus was very near indeed to him now.

On June 13, 1231, on Friday—the day of the week on which our Lord died—the friar said to Pedro, "It is too far a journey to carry me into St. Mary's in Padua. Yet I should like to die in a Franciscan house. The little friary of Arcella lies close by and is near the convent of the good nuns whom Father Francis formed into his Second Order under the holy Lady Clare."

Pedro and the others made a litter of boughs, and upon it they bore their Friar Anthony to Arcella. As he lay dying within its cool walls, he raised his hand in blessing over Pedro and the brothers and over the nuns who also stood there. Then he asked the brothers to sing for him. Thus it was that, amidst song which praised God, the young Anthony of Padua—Fernando of Portugal—finally closed his eyes. That was how, too, his Father Francis had died.

Less than a year later, in Rome, Anthony of Padua was proclaimed a saint. At that very hour, in faraway Lisbon, the bells of the cathedral where lay the cross in the stone carved by the fingers of a boy named Fernando, began to peal out over the city. Sir Juan, sitting with his wife in the garden, raised his head and listened.

"I wonder why the cathedral bells are ringing?" he asked. "It sounds as though a new saint had been made."

He walked up the hill to the church to inquire.

"It's very strange, Sir Juan," said the canon. "The bells just suddenly began to peal of themselves. No one rang them."

VISION BOOKS